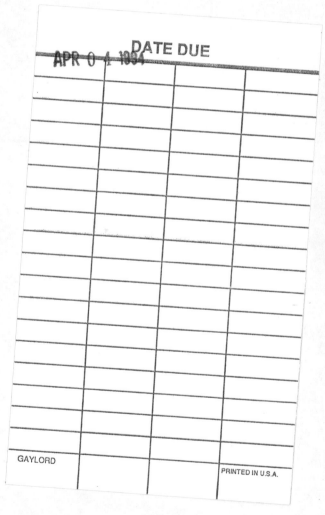

POLYMER REVIEWS

H. F. MARK *and* E. H. IMMERGUT, *Editors*

Additional volumes in preparation

INFRARED SPECTRA OF POLYMERS
in the medium and long wavelength regions

DIETER O. HUMMEL

Associate Professor of Physical Chemistry,
University of Cologne, Germany

INTERSCIENCE PUBLISHERS

a division of John Wiley & Sons

New York · London · Sydney

Those portions of the book which appeared as a Technical Documentary Report of the
U.S. Air Force may be reproduced for any purpose of the United States Government.

MADE AND PRINTED IN GREAT BRITAIN BY
WILLIAM CLOWES AND SONS LIMITED, LONDON AND BECCLES

Foreword

This book has its origin in a Technical Documentary Report of the U.S. Air Force to be used in practical infrared analysis of high polymers, resins, and related substances. I owe much gratitude both to the officials at Wright-Patterson Air Force Base, Ohio, and to Interscience Publishers who have enabled me to publish it in this form. Undoubtedly a publication of this kind, still determined for the analyst in an infrared laboratory, shows many signs of a compromise. It is more than a simple collection of spectra but it is not at all a comprehensive review of our present knowledge of the infrared spectra of polymers and other macromolecular compounds. The latter one is a task still to be done, and a very necessary one. In addition, our collection of spectra was restricted by the limited accessibility of samples.

For many years, at least for most spectroscopists, the infrared range closed with 15 μ, that is, with the range of the mainly used sodium chloride prisms. In the past few years, however, many laboratories were equipped with spectrographs covering also a considerable fraction of the long wavelength region. For them, and also for the others who intend to go beyond the usual range, the question occurs: what can we do in practical analysis with the additional 25 μ or 400 wavenumbers accessible by most of the modern spectrographs? An answer to this would be a collection of spectra in the long wavelength region together with elementary discussions about this range. This publication is an attempt to reach this goal.

The range between 15 and 40 μ (667 to 250 cm^{-1}) is not really part of the "far infrared." All the absorptions in this region are still fundamental vibrations, and there is no physical borderline around 15 μ. We therefore also included in the spectral part of this monograph the spectra in the conventional "medium infrared." The reason why these are linear in wavelengths whereas the spectra in the long wavelength range are linear in wavenumbers is purely historical: the latter ones were scanned with a Perkin–Elmer spectrograph mod. 102, whereas the former ones had to be scanned with a Leitz spectrograph IR III designed for linear wavelength registration.

A number of colleagues have considerably assisted me in this work. I owe many thanks to Mr. Freeman F. Bentley, Wright–Patterson Air Force Base, Ohio, who actually initiated this investigation. Most of the spectra in the rocksalt range were prepared by my collaborators Miss Rita Wilmers, Miss Heide Trein, Miss Burgunde Hirzinger, and Mrs. Elsbeth Zoschke. Most of the samples were kindly provided by Dr. Ival O. Salyer, Monsanto Research Corp., Dayton, Ohio, and by Dr. E. Trommsdorff, Röhm and Haas GmbH, Darmstadt, Germany. Finally I am most grateful to the Aeronautical Systems Division, Materials Central, Physics Branch, Ohio, to the "Deutsche Forschungsgemeinschaft," to the "Verband der Chemischen Industrie," and to the "Fachgruppe Kunststoffe und Kautschuk" of the "Gesellschaft Deutscher Chemiker" for their financial contributions.

Dieter O. Hummel

NOTE: Registered trade names were not generally marked in this book. This does not mean that they can be used freely.

Contents

I

Introduction

The great value of infrared spectroscopy in the structure elucidation and analysis of technical polymers and resins has been well established. Hausdorff[100] and Kagarise and Weinberger[126] were the first to publish collections of infrared spectra of technical polymers and resins. Krimm[151] studied the complete infrared spectra of eight different polymers. He made a complete vibrational analysis of these compounds and proposed possible structures. Hummel[111] has published two books on polymeric materials. One volume contains a comprehensive and systematic collection of spectra; the other gives a discussion of chemical and infrared spectroscopic methods for the identification of plastics, resins, and related materials. In 1961, Brown et al.[38] and Nyquist[240] published spectral data on newly synthesized polymers and resins. Quite recently Haslam and Willis[99a] published a book on the identification and analysis of polymers by chemical and infrared spectroscopic methods.

Most of the aforementioned authors' studies of polymers were limited to the NaCl range between 5000–667 cm^{-1}. This present volume reports the results of a study of polymers, resins, waxes, plasticizers, and monomers in the region of 700–250 cm^{-1}.

For the spectroscopist who is interested in molecular vibrations of polymers in terms of group theory and normal coordinate treatment, the authors who have discussed these topics are listed in the reference portion of this report (Krimm[151], Liang[163, 168], Higgs[106], Tadokoro[321]).

To date, there have been only a few publications on the spectra of plastics, resins, and related substances in the far infrared. Seifert and Randall[292] reported about the reflection spectra of several plastics. The spectrophotometer used was rather simple. Reststrahlen filters were used to produce monochromatic radiation, and transmittance and reflections were measured near 480, 340, 240, 195, 160, 120, 105, 80, and 60 cm^{-1}. The spectra depicted in the article were not useful for qualitative and quantitative analysis. Krimm showed the value of the far infrared spectra in the structure elucidation of high polymers in a number of his publications (see for instance, Krimm[151]). Hummel[113, 114] recently reported about his research on the identification of plastics, resins, monomers, plasticizers, solvents, and fibrous materials by the use of their far infrared spectra.

Spectra in the far infrared are sensitive to slight changes in structure and often contribute valuable information in identifying complex molecules and mixtures. Moreover, each additional absorption band in the far infrared complements the structural information already obtained with the rocksalt spectrum and results in a more reliable identification of a system.

Absorptions in the far infrared are mainly due to bending vibrations of the skeleton and to stretching and bending vibrations of heavy atoms such as the halogens, silicon, or metals. The transition energies are low, and interactions within and between molecules may have a strong influence on the frequency and intensity of certain absorption bands. This implies a sensitivity of far infrared spectra to the physical state of a substance and the conformation of its molecules. This is advantageous where polymers with the same chemical structure but different conformation or tacticity or crystallinity must be analyzed. On the other hand, strong but random interactions within and between polar molecules are clearly disadvantageous from an analytical aspect since they tend to produce a strong absorption background and a broadening of the absorption bands. All these factors affecting spectral features in the far infrared will be more fully explained in succeeding paragraphs.

As was mentioned previously, there are interactions within and between molecules which can affect a spectrum. These are intra- and intermolecular interactions. The former is initiated by mechanical as well as electrical coupling; the latter is usually of an electric nature: dipole–dipole interactions and van der Waals forces.

An example of very strong forces between the molecules is that of polyamides (polymers with intermolecular hydrogen bridges). Intermolecular forces are strongest in crystalline polymers. The vibrations in one molecule or monomer unit cannot be discussed without consideration of the same vibrations in the neighboring molecule or monomer unit. This close association between the molecules causes the well-known splitting of certain bands of crystalline polymers.

A familiar example of the influence of intramolecular interaction is the carbonyl stretching vibration. Its frequency position and intensity depends principally upon the polarity of the intramolecular environment. Weaker forces usually have too small an influence to be observed with bands of higher energy. However, the vibrations in the far infrared have a low vibrational energy and are much more liable to change in frequency position or intensity by weak forces. This influence is strongly heightened by a symmetrical conformation of the polymer chain, i.e. the repeating units being in the same plane or in an n-fold helix.

Three-dimensional crystallinity always causes a certain symmetry within the single polymer chains. On the other hand it seems likely that isotactic or syndiotactic configuration of a polymer forces the monomer units into a symmetrical arrangement independently of three-dimensional crystallinity. Isotactic configuration of the asymmetric carbon atoms in a chain usually produces a helical conformation in the chain. This conformation may be considered as a one-dimensional crystallinity, and may in certain cases exist even in an amorphous sample. Both effects have their influence on a spectrum. It is therefore possible to distinguish between "crystalline" (in the sense of three-dimensional crystallinity) and "tactic" absorption bands. The former ones disappear in molten or dissolved material, the latter ones remain if the conformation within the chain is unaltered during the melting or dissolving process. Polystyrene is a good example of a polymer which exhibits these effects. The bands at 565 cm^{-1} and 498 cm^{-1} of the crystalline material are very weak or disappear in dissolved or swollen isotactic polystyrene. These bands are apparently sensitive to crystallinity. On the other hand, an absorption band at 588 cm^{-1} is the same in the spectra of crystalline and amorphous isotactic polystyrene. It is not observed in the spectrum of atactic polystyrene. This band is apparently specific for isotacticity and is caused principally by intramolecular interactions.

As to the intensity of far infrared absorption bands, polymers and resins can be classified roughly into three groups. The first group includes molecules containing heavy polar atoms. Examples are halogenated polyhydrocarbons and silicones. These compounds have polar bonds and give rise to very strong absorption bands. Their spectra in the long wavelength region may be recorded as films 0.005 to 0.01 mm in thickness. The second group comprises practically all compounds with less heavy and polar heteroatoms like oxygen and nitrogen. Aromatic structures also are included in this group. Examples are polyesters, polyethers, phenolic resins, amino and amido resins, and aromatic polyhydrocarbons. These compounds give rise to absorption bands of medium intensity. Sample thicknesses around 0.1 mm are needed to obtain significant spectra. The third group consists of compounds having only structures of low polarity. Examples are aliphatic polyhydrocarbons of all kinds. These molecules usually have only weak absorption bands in the far infrared. Sample pathlengths between 0.3 mm and several millimeters are needed. The lower value holds for polymers with high sterical order, especially crystalline ones.

II

Experimental

A. Apparatus

The spectra shown in this report were recorded with a Perkin–Elmer Spectrophotometer Model 102 described by Marshall.[181] To reduce the loss of energy due to atmospheric absorption, the entire instrument was purged with dry nitrogen. The wavenumber reproducibility is 1 cm^{-1} over the entire range.

In the present work, many of the spectra of samples were scanned using devices such as screens or cells with paraffin oil or solvents in the reference beam to compensate for absorption background and scattered light. Therefore, these spectra can only be used on a qualitative basis since the transmittances may not be true.

Sometimes water bands are evident in the spectra (indicated by × on spectrum) even though purging of the instrument with nitrogen was carried out. These are not to be confused with sample absorption bands. Therefore, a spectrum of water vapor is depicted in Figure 1 and band positions are enumerated in Table 1.

TABLE 1. Wavenumbers of Pure Rotational Lines of Water Vapor (Rao et al.[262a])

550.00	506.94	456.87	398.97	358.49	323.92
547.81	502.26	452.89	397.34	357.27	323.67
546.30	492.05	446.93	394.28	354.60	315.08
545.29	486.12	443.70	385.54	354.19	303.02
541.07	483.97	436.46	384.88	351.21	298.42
536.25	472.75	434.82	383.82	349.77	289.46
525.97	472.20	431.16	376.27	343.21	282.72
519.60	467.93	425.34	375.38	340.45	277.94
517.77	461.45	423.03	374.54	335.16	266.94*
516.81	452.73	419.88	370.02	327.60	221.74*

* These figures are taken from the work of Randall et al.[262]. Only the most intense bands are reported here.

B. Materials

Most of the materials used were contributed by the manufacturers and are of a technical grade. The plasticizers and monomers originated partly from a collection owned by the Monsanto Research Corporation, Dayton, Ohio, and partly from the Institut für Physikalische Chemie und Kolloidchemie, University of Cologne, Cologne, Germany. All of the eutactic polymers, with the exception of isotactic polypropylene, were research samples contributed by Röhm und Haas GmbH, Darmstadt, Germany, and by Monsanto Chemical Company, St. Louis, Missouri. The solvents used were of analytical grade.

C. Preparation of Samples

The infrared spectra of polymers studied in this report were obtained as films cast from solutions, pressed or melted films, microtomed samples, paraffin oil mulls, or as KBr disks.

1. FILMS CAST FROM SOLUTIONS

The majority of the polymers studied were recorded as films. The films were prepared by dissolving these compounds in a suitable organic solvent (see individual spectra for solvents used), pouring them onto a glass plate, and evaporating off the solvent. If the films adhered too tightly to the surface of the glass, they were heated with water until they could be drawn off. All films were finally dried in an oil-vacuum at slightly elevated temperatures.

Resins were cast directly on cesium bromide plates approximately 5 mm in thickness. To check if interfering bands were present due to these plates in the region of 700–250 cm^{-1}, a spectrum was recorded (Figure 2).

In the case of polyamides, formic acid was used as a solvent. Sometimes opaque films resulted which were difficult to handle. To correct this, these films were soaked with paraffin oil while still on the glass plate and then carefully removed with the help of a razor blade to a cesium bromide plate. The spectra of the samples were recorded and compensation for the paraffin oil adhering to the film was made by placing an equivalent amount of oil on a CsBr plate in the reference beam.

Polymers, like polyoxymethylene, were dissolved in dimethyl sulfoxide. Then they were precipitated by adding methanol or ethanol to the solution. The precipitate was washed at least five times to remove the high boiling solvent and then dried in a vacuum oven to remove the alcohol. The resulting dried powder was prepared for recording by using either KBr or mulling techniques.

Polymers often retain the solvents used to prepare films. Drying in a vacuum oven at elevated temperatures most of the time was sufficient to drive them off. Sometimes, however, extraction with a low-boiling non-solvent for the polymer had to be employed. Water was found to be an efficient extractant for dimethylformamide and dimethyl sulfoxide. Anhydrous ethanol can be used for the extraction of benzene.

There are a few publications on the far infrared absorptions of solvents. Stanevich and Yaroslavsky[314] reported the absorption spectra of carbon tetrachloride, chloroform, benzene, dioxane, and of polyethylene in the region 20–2,000 μ. Wyss *et al.*[355] discussed the far infrared spectra of twelve organic liquids including benzene, chlorobenzene, bromobenzene, toluene, carbon tetrachloride, chloroform, methylene chloride, carbon disulphide, paraffin oil, *n*-hexane, cyclohexane, and pyridine in the liquid state.

2. PRESSED OR MELTED FILMS

Non-polar polymers, like polyethylene, require sample thicknesses up to a few millimeters in order to obtain a significant spectrum. Films of these thicknesses are best prepared in a die, heated at a temperature about 20°C above the softening temperature of the polymer. Since many polymers will oxidize at higher temperatures, the pressing should be done in an inert atmosphere. If a high degree of crystallinity in the polymer sample is desired, the cooling is done quite slowly. Quenched samples can be crystallized by heating them about 20° below their melting point for a few hours.

With some caution it is possible to prepare a film between cesium bromide plates. The plates are first preheated on a heating stage to a temperature just above the melting point of the polymer. The plates are taken apart with a pair of tongs and the beads or scraps are put on one of the plates and immediately covered by the other. Pressing of the so-called sandwich with a cork produces the desired film. Fortunately, cesium bromide and iodide are not as sensitive to sudden temperature changes as sodium chloride. However, these plates can deform at higher temperatures and caution must be taken when applying the technique just described.

Stereoregular poly-α-olefins have high melting points and are subject to oxidation. If a suitable die is unavailable, the finely divided polymer is mixed with paraffin oil into a thick slurry. The slurry is placed between cesium bromide plates and heated slowly. Part of the paraffin oil seeps out, leaving the polymer in the form of a soft, rubbery sheet. The degree of crystallinity in a sample is reduced by this handling procedure.

A very helpful method of using polyethylene as dispersing material was described by May and Schwing[186]. The authors mix 2–3 mg of sample with 50 mg of low-melting polyethylene powder, such as Epolene C (Eastman products) and melt this mixture between two cover slips on the heating block of a melting point apparatus. Finely dispersed polyethylene can be prepared by dissolving polyethylene pellets in hot xylene, letting the solution cool to room temperature, and then precipitating the rest of the polyethylene with ethanol. The filtered product is washed with ethanol and dried. If the sample decomposes at higher temperatures powdered mixtures of polyethylene and low-melting paraffin can be used.

Since polyethylene shows only very weak absorptions in the far infrared region the method described above can be used to obtain the far infrared spectra of all kinds of solid materials.

3. MICROTOMED SAMPLES

Polymers such as vulcanized rubbers, cured polyester resins, and polytetrafluoroethylene, will not dissolve in conventional solvents or melt when heated. Consequently, these polymers, if of the right pliability, can be cut into thin slices of suitable thickness without prior treatment using a microtome. Some rubbers and very soft materials have to be cooled in a dry ice–acetone mixture to obtain a certain degree of rigidity before microtoming can be accomplished. Hard polymers are plasticized with suitable swelling agents before cutting.

4. PARAFFIN OIL MULLS

Paraffin oil or "Nujol" exhibits only weak absorptions in the 700–300 cm^{-1} region (Figure 176). This makes it an ideal carrier for finely divided compounds. Good spectra have been obtained for polyoxymethylene (Delrin), polyamides, stereoregular poly-α-olefins, and polyvinyl chloride using the mull technique. Compensation for the paraffin oil in these samples can be accomplished by using a comparable amount of oil in the reference beam.

5. KBr DISKS

Thin disks of potassium bromide are transparent to about 250 cm^{-1} (40 microns). Hence, they can be used as carriers for materials in the far infrared. Unfortunately, large concentrations of samples are often required which results in turbid or opaque disks. If compensation for the scattered light is not possible through the use of screens, a lower concentration of sample is employed and scale expansion utilized. Insoluble, hard materials can be reduced to a fine powder or shavings by scraping their surfaces with a razor blade. Devaney and Thompson[63] recommend the use of a diamond spatula. After the polymer is in this state, the KBr technique is applied.

III

Results

The infrared spectra of 191 polymers, resins, waxes, plasticizers, monomers, and solvents have been investigated in the ranges 2.5–15 μ, and 700–250 cm^{-1}. All these compounds have been separated into chemically related groups and their spectra discussed with regard to their analytical use in chemical and structural problems.

A. Aliphatic Polyhydrocarbons (Chart I)

A thorough study of the far infrared spectra of aliphatic hydrocarbons was published by Bentley and Wolfarth.[23] Our findings concerning aliphatic polyhydrocarbons in this investigation are, to a certain degree, in agreement with their observations. Straight-chain paraffins of high molecular weight have just one band around 540 cm^{-1} which is strong enough to be observed in samples 2 mm thick. Branched alkanes have around four bands which are stronger, intensity-wise, than the one observed for the straight-chain polymers recorded at the same thickness. Hence, poly-α-olefins can easily be distinguished from polyethylenes.

It is important to remember that the bands found in polymer spectra are not only due to their physical state but also are the result of orientation effects. The spectra of polymers with a certain steric order within the chain, like the eutactic poly-α-olefins, or with a certain degree of three-dimensional crystallinity have to be discussed in terms of symmetry elements and group theory. A method for the determination of normal vibrations of polymer molecules with a helical configuration was described by Tadokoro.[321] This method is also applicable to molecules with an infinitely extended planar zigzag-chain such as crystalline polyethylene.

1. SATURATED POLYHYDROCARBONS

a. *Polyethylene*

There are two types of polyethylenes, namely, high-pressure polyethylene (low-density) and low-pressure polyethylene (high-density). The former is produced by a process developed by ICI of England and is a branched polymer. It contains both short (mainly C_2H_5 and n-C_4H_9) and long side-chains. The latter type of polyethylene is produced by the Ziegler method or by other processes applying low pressures of ethylene and special catalysts. This product is unbranched.

The nature of short-chain branches in polyethylenes was studied by a number of authors. Bryant and Voter[40] used the methyl absorption at 7.25 μ (1379 cm^{-1}) and the absorption of ethyl groups at 11.2 μ (893 cm^{-1}) for the determination of end groups in different polyethylenes. Harlen et al.[96] found that irradiation of polyethylene leads to a selective removal of the short side-chains in the polymers. These appear in the gaseous products of the radiolysis as saturated hydrocarbons and can be analyzed by mass spectrometry or gas chromatography. The results strongly suggest that high-pressure polyethylene contains mainly C_2 and C_4 side-chains and no appreciable amount of C_1 and C_3 side-chains. This was confirmed by Willbourn[350] who reported absolute methods for the determination of side groups in polyethylenes. Harvey and Ketley[98] finally reported characteristic infrared bands for short-chain branches in polyolefins.

The infrared spectra of the different types of polyethylene have been studied in greater detail than those of most other polymers. Rugg et al.[273] studied the infrared spectra of a number of high-pressure polyethylenes and found that as molecular weight increases the degree of branching decreases. They found also that the degree of unsaturation decreases with increasing molecular weight. Three types of double bond groups were present, i.e. $RHC{=}CH_2$, $RHC{=}CHR$, $RRC{=}CH_2$. Krimm, Liang, and Sutherland[157] obtained the infrared spectrum of high-pressure polyethylene between 3000 cm^{-1} and 70 cm^{-1}. Assignments of the fundamentals were made with the help of the group theory analysis. Independently Nielsen and Woollett[234] published a very thorough study on the vibrational spectra of polyethylenes and related substances. The authors published Raman spectra and infrared spectra of a variety of polyethylenes of different crystallinities and branching. The fundamentals of the unit cell of crystalline polyethylene were assigned. More information and literature references on the infrared spectra of polyethylenes may be found in a review written by Wood and Luongo[353].

Concerning the far infrared region, Rugg et al.[273] were the first to observe weak and complex bands in the spectrum of high-pressure polyethylene with maxima at about 591 cm^{-1} (16.9 μ) and 558 cm^{-1} (17.9 μ). They gave as a probable assignment of this group of band structures the general type —CH_2—$CHRR'$, R and R' being methyl, ethyl, or propyl groups. Borello and Mussa[32] interpreted these absorption maxima and an additional band at 543 cm^{-1} (18.4 μ), as a pure methyl band system.* Krimm et al.[151, 156] also found weak bands in the far infrared spectrum of high-pressure polyethylene. Our own results for polyethylenes (Figures 3a and 3b) are tabulated along with Krimm's in Table 2. Tentative assignments are made for some of the vibrations.

TABLE 2. Far Infrared Absorption Bands of Polyethylenes (PE)

| Krimm[151] (cm^{-1}) | This report | | Probable assignment |
	High-pressure PE (cm^{-1})	Marlex 50 (cm^{-1})	
—	—	630	—CH=CH$_2$
600	—	—	—
573	585	570	—
—	—	549	—CH=CH$_2$
543	538	—	Skeleton vibration involving CH$_3$
—	—	450	—
430	425	430	—
200	Not studied	Not studied	—

Bands near 630 and 549 cm^{-1} in Marlex 50 were tentatively assigned to a vibration of terminal vinyl groups. This seems reasonable since these bands were also found by Bentley and Wolfarth[23] in alkenes having this same terminal grouping. The band at 538 cm^{-1} found in the spectrum of high-pressure polyethylene has already been assigned by Rugg et al.[273] and Borello and Mussa[32] as being due to a skeleton vibration involving methyl groups. Our spectral data are in agreement with their assignment based on relative band intensities at 540 cm^{-1}. Branched polyethylenes show a more intense band than the unbranched. This is logical since the former contains a higher concentration of methyl groups (20–30 per 1000 carbon atoms) than the latter (less than 1.5 methyl groups per 1000 carbon atoms). Bentley and Wolfarth[23] observed a band at 538 cm^{-1} in long-chain alkanes. The intensity of the band decreased with increasing chain length which is consistent with our findings above.

b. Polypropylene

Propylene can be polymerized with Lewis acids yielding low molecular weight oils or amorphous, rubber-like materials. Ziegler-type catalysts,

---

* Willis et al.[351] investigated the far infrared spectra of six different linear and branched polyethylenes between 450 cm^{-1} and 40 cm^{-1} with respect to their proposed use as window materials for far infrared cells. There were remarkable differences between the spectra; however, most of them showed absorption bands near 430, 290, 200, and 75 cm^{-1}.

for example, complexes of titanium halides with aluminum alkyls, cause the formation of high molecular weight, crystalline polymers which have gained wide application in industry. These polymers have a stereoregular structure with respect to the asymmetric* carbon atoms in the chain. According to Natta[219], vinyl polymers with the same steric configuration, d or l, of the asymmetric carbon atoms in the chains are called "isotactic"; those with an alternating configuration of the consecutive asymmetric carbon atoms giving d, l, d, l sequences are called "syndiotactic." "Atactic" vinyl polymers do not have any regularity in the distribution of the configurations of the asymmetric carbon atoms along a polymer chain. A discussion of the definition of an atactic vinyl polymer with respect to polypropylenes was given by Folt et al.[75]

Propylene can be polymerized by Friedel–Crafts catalysts according to a cationic mechanism. The resulting polymers (usually having a low molecular weight) in their structure probably come closest to being atactic. However, during the polymerization process numerous isomerization and chain transfer processes occur and give rise to a highly irregular polymer. Cationically produced polypropylene shows rather weak absorption bands at 1155 cm^{-1} (8.65 μ) and 970 cm^{-1} (10.3 μ) and therefore has only a low content of head-to-tail structures. According to Ketley and Harvey[139], polypropylene which was prepared at $-78°C$ with Al_2Br_6/HBr contains a considerable percentage of ethyl and propyl side-groups. These groups are characterized by absorptions at 769 cm^{-1} (13.0 μ) and 739 cm^{-1} (13.42 μ). Atactic polypropylenes of different kinds were also investigated by Liang and Watt[174] and Immergut et al.[118]

Atactic polypropylene which was prepared by stereospecific catalysts is of the normal head-to-tail type and probably at least partly isotactic. It is amorphous and contains no (or only a small amount of) helical structures. In addition to the head-to-tail sequences there seems to be a small percentage of head-to-head tail-to-tail arrangements being characterized by absorptions near 751, 917, and 1110 cm^{-1} (13.3, 10.9, and 9 μ, see van Schooten and Mostert[290]). In the far infrared, the spectrum of atactic polypropylene (Figure 4) shows a broad band with maxima at 575 cm^{-1} and 557 cm^{-1}. These bands probably are due to the skeleton vibrations involving the methyl side-groups. Tobin[341] also found a broad absorption band between 460 cm^{-1} and 620 cm^{-1} with a maximum at 542 cm^{-1} with a similar type polypropylene.

---

* Actually, the differently-substituted C atom in a monomer unit of a vinyl chain is pseudo-asymmetric since the two chain-like substituents of different length can only formally be considered as different. Isotactic polymers therefore are not optically active.

Natta *et al.*[227] stated that there are three different types of stereo-regular, crystallizable polypropylenes as follows.

1. Isotactic head-to-tail polypropylene, characterized by a helical structure of the chain with three monomer units per repeat and by a melting temperature of 170°C.

2. Syndiotactic head-to-tail polypropylene, characterized by a "double helix" of the chain with four monomer units per repeat, and by a melting temperature very close to that of the isotactic material.

3. Head-to-head and tail-to-tail polypropylene produced by alternating copolymerization of ethylene and *cis*-1-butene.

One of these, isotactic polypropylene, is produced technically in large quantities. It is capable of crystallizing into different polymorphous modifications (Padden and Keith[242], Addink and Beintema[2]). Due to the low intermolecular forces these different forms have the same infrared spectrum. The infrared spectra of normal and deuterated isotactic polypropylenes, either crystalline or amorphous, oriented and unoriented, were studied by a number of authors. Important investigations were contributed by Peraldo[246], Abe and Yanagisawa[1], Heinen[103], Liang and Pearson[173], Liang, Lytton and Boone[170,171], Luongo[178], McDonald and Ward[180], Miyazawa *et al.*[197,203] and others. The unit cell of crystalline isotactic polypropylene is monoclinic and contains four helical chains. Each chain has a threefold screw axis as the only symmetry element.

The far infrared spectrum of crystalline isotactic polypropylene was extensively studied by Miyazawa and his collaborators[197–201,204]. Other

TABLE 3. Far Infrared Bands of Isotactic and Atactic Polypropylenes

Atactic		Isotactic, Amorphous	Isotactic, Crystalline		
Tobin[341] (cm^{-1})	This report (cm^{-1})	This report (cm^{-1})	Tobin[341] (cm^{-1})	This report (cm^{-1})	Miyazawa et al.[199] (cm^{-1})
—	—	315 (w)	—	312 (?)(vw)	106
—	—	—	408 (vw)	390 (w)	155
460–620 (br)	475 (?, vw)	455 (m)	460 (w)	453 (m)	169
—	520 (vw)	475 (m, sh)	537 (w)	527 (m)	210–200
542	557 (m)	550–575 (w, br)	580 (vw)	575 (vw, br, sh)	251
—	575 (m, br)	—			321
		615			398
—	643 (w)	—			458
—	690 (w)	694			528
					575

Symbols: w = weak; vw = very weak; sh = shoulder; m = medium; br = broad.

investigators were Tobin[341] and Gramberg[91]. The results of these authors, together with our own, are shown in Table 3. All of the far infrared absorption bands of crystalline isotactic polypropylene belong to strongly coupling skeleton vibrations; the calculated assignments are given by Miyazawa et al.

In the far infrared spectrum of a cationic polypropylene with no steric order at all (Figure 4), there is only one complex band, broadened by random mechanical coupling of this bending vibration with other chain vibrations.

Isotactic configuration of the asymmetric carbon atoms primarily introduces a short-range order, whether helical or not, and consequently, defines interactions between the monomer units. This has a strong influence on the frequency of the C—C—C bending vibration and on its envelope, too. The rather distinct far infrared spectrum of an amorphous but partly isotactic polypropylene (Figure 5) in its characteristics is situated between a cationic polypropylene and a crystallinic isotactic polypropylene.

Isotactic polypropylene was proposed as a window material for far infrared cells at higher temperatures (Willis et al.[351]).

Syndiotactic polypropylene was described by Natta et al.[229, 230] and is probably identical to the modification of polypropylene found by Addink and Beintema[2]. Its spectrum in the rocksalt range is very similar to that of isotactic polypropylene. It is distinguished only by a band at 867 cm^{-1} not occurring in the spectrum of the isotactic material. No data in the far infrared are available for syndiotactic polypropylene.

Disyndiotactic head-to-head tail-to-tail polypropylene was described by Natta et al.[230] Its spectrum has not been published so far.

c. Poly-1-butene

Complexes of titanium halides with aluminum alkyls or other catalysts described by Ziegler and Natta generally polymerize 1-alkenes into stereoregular polymers. With 1-butene a crystalline isotactic polymer is formed which differs in its chemical structure from isotactic polypropylene only by the side groups, i.e. ethyl groups are present instead of methyl. The crystal structure of the most stable form of poly-1-butene was described by Natta et al.[224] It is very similar to that of isotactic polystyrene and isotactic polypropylene. The unit cell is rhombohedral and contains eighteen monomer units in six helices. There are three monomer units in one repeat. The strongest band at 533 cm^{-1} in its far infrared spectrum (Figure 7) is probably due to the C—C—C bending vibration involving the tertiary carbon atom. The infrared spectrum of poly-1-butene was published by Tadokoro *et al.*[323]; a complete vibrational analysis has not yet been published.

d. *Polyisobutene*

The monomer unit of polyisobutene,

$$-CH_2-\underset{\underset{CH_3}{|}}{\overset{\overset{CH_3}{|}}{C}}-$$

does not contain an asymmetric carbon atom. The only possibilities of a regular structure are, therefore, head-to-tail and head-to-head tail-to-tail arrangements of the monomer units in the chains. The infrared spectra of BF_3 polymerized samples were studied by Dainton and Sutherland[56]. According to these authors, polyisobutene is a head-to-tail polymer with mainly *t*-butyl and isopropene groups as end-groups:

$$H_3C-\underset{\underset{CH_3}{|}}{\overset{\overset{CH_3}{|}}{C}}\left(CH_2-\underset{\underset{CH_3}{|}}{\overset{\overset{CH_3}{|}}{C}}\right)_n\underset{}{\overset{\overset{CH_3}{|}}{C}}=CH_2$$

Nelson[233] studied the infrared absorptions of the CH groups in polyisobutene. The infrared spectrum of irradiated polyisobutene was published by Higgins[105]. Fuller *et al.*[82] studied the chain structure by the x-ray fiber patterns and found a fiber period of 18.63 Å. The repeating unit along the chain contains eight monomer units arranged in a helix.

The far infrared spectrum of polyisobutene (Figure 8) shows only weak absorption bands. A band around 510 cm^{-1}, according to Bentley and Wolfarth[23], is characteristic for 3,3-disubstituted alkanes. A corresponding band is found in the spectrum of polyisobutene at 527 cm^{-1}. Like other highly branched hydrocarbons, polyisobutene shows a number of other absorption bands in the far infrared whose assignment to certain skeleton vibrations is not as yet clarified.

e. *Poly-(4-methyl-1-pentene)*

In certain cases, also branched 1-alkenes can be polymerized with stereospecific catalysts of the Ziegler type. Poly-(4-methyl-1-pentene) was obtained by this process, and is a highly crystalline, high-melting polymer with an isotactic configuration of the asymmetric carbon atoms. The far infrared spectrum (Figure 9) is rather similar to that of crystalline isotactic polypropylene (Figure 6). It is not unlikely that this is due to a bending vibration of the isopropyl side-group

which is similar to the bending vibration of the methyl side-groups of amorphous and crystalline isotactic polypropylene. Also, the splitting into three components may be due to a similar structure of the helical chains. Poly-(4-methyl-1-pentene) was proposed as a window material for far infrared cells at higher temperatures (Willis *et al.*[351]).

2. UNSATURATED POLYHYDROCARBONS

a. *Polybutadienes*

Polybutadiene obtained with radical initiation or by other non-stereospecific catalysts contains three different, atactic steric structures in its chains:

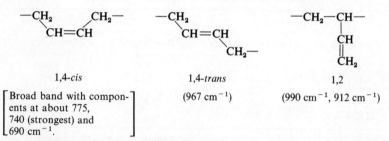

1,4-*cis*	1,4-*trans*	1,2
Broad band with components at about 775, 740 (strongest) and 690 cm^{-1}.	(967 cm^{-1})	(990 cm^{-1}, 912 cm^{-1})

The most characteristic bands of these unsaturated groups originate from out-of-plane vibrations of the hydrogen atoms attached to the double bond (Rasmussen and Brattain[263], Sheppard and Sutherland[297]).

The fractions of the three different structures in conventional polybutadienes vary within certain limits with the kind of catalyst, and with the reaction temperature. A number of infrared spectrophotometric methods for the quantitative determination of the different monomer units in polybutadienes were published (Hampton[95], Binder[25], Kimmer and Schmalz[140], Silas *et al.*[306], Schmalz and Geiseler[282, 283], and Kastorskii and Medinkova[130]).

Conventional polybutadienes are amorphous and are either low molecular weight oils or higher molecular weight elastomers. By the application of stereospecific catalysts, butadiene can be polymerized to yield four different highly crystalline and highly stereoregular polymers: 1,4-*cis*; 1,4-*trans*; 1,2-isotactic; and 1,2-syndiotactic polybutadiene.

Preparation and properties of *cis*-1,4-polybutadiene were described by Natta et al.[231] The compound *trans*-1,4-polybutadiene can be obtained by certain catalyst systems (Natta et al.[230, 229]), or by isomerization of *cis*- or mixed *cis–trans*-polybutadiene under the influence of ultraviolet (Golub[89]) or γ-radiation (Golub[87, 88]) and in the presence of stabilizers. The reaction product still contains about 5% *cis* units. Crystalline 1,4-*trans*-polybutadiene occurs in two different enantiomorphous modifications (Natta et al.[229]). Nikitin et al.[235] studied these modifications more closely and found a temperature range of 55–70°C for the transformation of modification I into modification II. The latter melts between 110°C and 130°C. Isotactic and syndiotactic 1,2-polybutadiene were prepared by Wilke[349] and by Natta and his collaborators[228, 232].

The infrared spectra of the stereoregular polybutadienes were studied by several authors (Morero et al.[208], Nikitin et al.[235], Golub and Shipman[90], and Binder[25, 27]). Table 4 shows the infrared bands of 1,4-*trans*-

TABLE 4. Infrared Bands of 1,4-*trans*-Polybutadiene*

"Crystalline bands"		"Amorphous bands"	
Wavelength (μ)	Wavenumber (cm^{-1})	Wavelength (μ)	Wavenumber (cm^{-1})
7.49	1335	7.43	1346
8.10 I + II	1235	7.65	1307
8.92	1121		
9.49 I	1054		
12.93 I	773		

* These bands are sensitive to changes in crystallinity. The Roman numerals I and II denote the two crystal modifications.

polybutadiene which are sensitive to changes in crystallinity according to Nikitin and co-authors[235]. Fairly strong bands at 9.49 and 9.93 microns mainly arise from the crystalline modification I whereas the band at 8.10 microns arises partly from modification I and partly from modification II. Table 5 shows the bands above 10 microns characteristic for isotactic or syndiotactic 1,2-polybutadienes in the crystalline state according to Morero et al.[208]

Golub and Shipman[90] were the first to investigate the far infrared absorptions of 1,4-polybutadienes and various deuterated 1,4-polybutadienes. They prepared the *cis*-1,4-polybutadienes by a stereospecific catalyst and the *trans* isomers by isomerization of the *cis* isomers by ultraviolet light. In Table 6, the figures found by Golub and Shipman[90] are compared with our own. The samples of the former authors were cast from benzene solutions. It appears from their spectra that the samples

TABLE 5. Bands below 1000 cm^{-1} Characteristic of Isotactic or Syndiotactic 1,2-Polybutadienes in the Crystalline State*

Isotactic		Syndiotactic	
Wavelength (μ)	Wavenumber (cm^{-1})	Wavelength (μ)	Wavenumber (cm^{-1})
10.6	943	—	—
11.3	885	—	—
14.4†	694	15.0	667

* Bands common to both were omitted.
† Also in solution, but weaker.

were amorphous. The sample of a conventional atactic polybutadiene examined in this report (Figure 10) and the sample of a high *cis* polybutadiene (Figure 11) were also amorphous. The *trans*-1,4-polybutadiene (Figure 12), however, crystallized during the drying of the film in a vacuum oven. The two sharp and distinct bands at 440 cm^{-1} and 375 cm^{-1} of the crystalline *trans*-1,4-polybutadiene (modification I) does not appear in the spectrum of a dissolved or amorphous sample, and may, therefore, also be used for the determination of crystallinity (compare Nikitin *et al.*[235] and Table 4).

TABLE 6. Far Infrared Bands of 1,4-Polybutadienes

1,4-*cis*		1,4-*trans*		Conventional polybutadiene (mixture of isomers)
Golub and Shipman (cm^{-1})	This report (cm^{-1})	Golub and Shipman* (cm^{-1})	This report† (cm^{-1})	This report (cm^{-1})
702 (vw)	approx. 700 (m, b)	700 (w)‡	—	680–730 (m, b)
625 (w)	580–625 (w, vb)	600 (vw, b)	580–600 (vw, b)	580 (w)
600 (vw, b)				
	520 (w, b)			
	470 (w, b)			480 (b)
			440 (m)	
	390 (w, b)			
			375 (m)	

Symbols: m = medium; w = weak; vw = very weak; b = broad; vb = very broad.
* The sample was probably amorphous.
† Crystalline sample.
‡ Probably *cis*-isomer.

2

Unfortunately, amorphous *cis*-1,4-polybutadiene has practically no far infrared absorptions which are of any analytical value. The only analytical band for a direct determination of the *cis* content of polybutadienes is still that at about 740 cm^{-1}.

Far infrared data of crystalline *cis*-1,4-polybutadiene and 1,2-poly-butadienes are not available to date.

b. *Polyisoprenes*

2-Substituted 1,3-butadienes of the type

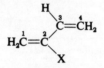

polymerize according to four different mechanisms, yielding four different isomeric structures:

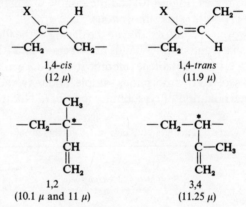

The wavelengths given for the different structures denote the absorption maxima of the hydrogen out-of-plane vibrations of the unsaturated group in amorphous polyisoprenes (X = CH$_3$). The position of these maxima depends on the type of the substituent X (compare polychlorobutadiene, X = Cl) and also on the physical state of the compound. Both 1,2- and 3,4-polyisoprenes contain asymmetric carbon atoms—in the formulas denoted with asterisks—and consequently are able to form isotactic and syndiotactic chains.

All natural polyisoprenes are 1,4-polymers and stereoregular within the chains. Hevea rubber is a *cis*-1,4-polyisoprene; gutta-percha and balata are *trans*-1,4-polyisoprenes. The band at 888 cm^{-1} (11.25 μ) is not due to 3,4-units as was formerly supposed (Salomon and van der Schee[276], and Fraga[79]). The natural polyisoprenes contain certain amounts of resinous compounds and polypeptides; hence they must be purified prior to their spectroscopic examination.

Isoprene can be polymerized by radicals, alkali metals, "Alfin" catalysts, and Lewis acids. The products obtained by these methods are not stereoregular but contain various amounts of the different isomeric monomer units in the polymer chains. The portion of these isomeric units in a polymer depends on the type of catalyst and also on the polymerization temperature. Alkali metals yield fairly uniform polymers. Sodium polyisoprene, for example, contains mainly 3,4-units. Lithium metal and trialkylaluminum–titanium halide complexes are stereospecific and thus allow the preparation of sterically uniform polymers. The first "synthetic natural rubbers" with a pure *cis*-1,4-structure produced in a technical scale were "Ameripol SN" (Horne *et al.*[109]) and "Coral Rubber" (Stavely *et al.*[316]).

The infrared spectrum of natural and synthetic polyisoprenes was studied by a large number of authors (Saunders and Smith[278], Dinsmore and Smith[64], Sutherland and Jones[320], Richardson and Sacher[269], Field *et al.*[74], Pokrovskii and Wolkenstein[253], Tkač and Kello[338], Dasgupta *et al.*[58], Stolka *et al.*[317], and Binder[26, 28]). The quantative analysis of different polyisoprenes was studied by Binder and Ransaw[28], Schmalz and Geiseler[282, 283], and Ciampelli *et al.*[51]). Recently Kössler and Vodehnal[147, 148] and Vodehnal and Kössler[343, 344] described quantitative methods for the determination of the different structures in polyisoprenes. *cis*-1,4-Polyisoprene crystallizes when stretched or at low temperatures. The velocity of crystallization is fastest at $-26°C$. The most obvious changes in the infrared spectrum during crystallization is the shift of the $=C-H$ γ-vibration from 11.95 μ to about 11.8 μ and the shift of a skeleton vibration at 8.8 μ to about 8.9 μ .The absorptivity of both bands is higher in the crystalline state.

The infrared spectrum of amorphous *trans*-1,4-polyisoprene (gutta-percha) is very similar to that of amorphous *cis*-1,4-polyisoprene. The main differences are listed below:

trans-1,4-polyisoprene	*cis-1,4-polyisoprene*
11.9 μ, 12.4 μ (doublet)	11.95 μ (s)
—	9.9 μ
8.65 μ (m)	8.8 μ (m)

trans-1,4-Polyisoprene crystallizes in two modifications. The α-form is stable at room temperature, and is the "natural" form of gutta-percha. It can be transformed into the β-form by heating the sample above 65°C and subsequent quenching. The α-form is characterized by sharp bands at about 11.35 μ, 11.6 μ, and 12.45 μ; β-gutta-percha by bands at 11.4 μ, 12.6 μ, and 13.3 μ. According to Horne et al.[109], a content of more than 10% trans-1,4-structures in cis-1,4-polyisoprene can be revealed by spectral differences in the range between 8 μ and 10.5 μ.

Semon et al.[293, 294] studied perdeuterio cis-1,4-polyisoprene and found an absorption band at 15.2 μ which is a $=$C—D γ-vibration and corresponds to the vibration at about 12 μ in the proteo cis-1,4-polyisoprene.

Saunders and Smith[278] were the first to publish data on the far infrared spectra of polyisoprenes. Horne et al.[109] measured the far infrared absorptions of natural and synthetic cis-1,4-polyisoprene. The spectra of these authors are collected in Table 7 together with our own results (see

TABLE 7. Far Infrared Bands of Polyisoprenes (cm^{-1})

cis-1,4				trans-1,4*				
Amorphous			Crystalline	Amorphous		Crystalline		
						α	β	
(a)	(b)	(c)	(a)	(a)	(c)	(a)	(a)	(c)
								680
					(650?)			665
						613		
							602	
						596		596
	595 (sh)	595 (sh)		595				
593 (sh)								
					590			
575	575							
		570						
				568 (sh)				
			565					
							562	
					560	559		558
500	510	500		500	515	526	(530?)	
			492		490	490		
				480	475		475	
						469		465
		420–30		455	447			415
		350						

(a) Saunders and Smith.[278] (b) Horne et al.[109] (c) This report. Symbol: sh = shoulder.
* Technical grade Balata, probably partly crystalline.

Figures 14–17). The strongest band in all spectra occurs between 570 cm^{-1} and 600 cm^{-1} and is very likely a C$=$C—CH$_3$ bending vibration. Another fairly intense band, some 70–100 wavenumbers lower, is probably a C$=$C—CH$_2$ vibration, coupling with the first one. The other bands may belong to C—C—C bending vibrations.

B. Aromatic Polyhydrocarbons (Chart II)

1. GENERAL REMARKS ON THE INFRARED ABSORPTIONS OF AROMATIC COMPOUNDS

The infrared spectra of benzene and its derivatives have been widely studied. Useful in the structure evaluation of aromatics are bands sensitive to positions of substituents and types of substituents.

Shimanouchi et al.[299] determined the normal coordinates for the out-of-plane C—H vibrations of benzene derivatives which proved to be sensitive to the type of substitution. Wiberley and Gonzalez[348] studied the infrared spectra of polynuclear aromatic compounds in the C—H stretching and out-of-plane bending regions and found valuable spectra structure correlations. Young et al.[357] found that the overtones and combination vibrations of the hydrogen out-of-plane vibrations of aromatics occurring between about 5 μ and 6 μ are characteristic for the type of substitution. Later, these bands were studied more fundamentally by Whiffen[347].

Lebas[161] investigated the vibrational spectra of a number of mono-substituted benzene derivatives in the range between 700 cm^{-1} and 200 cm^{-1}. Bogomolov[29-31], in a series of papers on the vibrational spectra of aromatic compounds, published calculated and experimental data on the characteristic vibrations of meta-substituted and para-disubstituted benzene derivatives. A paper by Garrigou-Lagrange et al.[84] was also concerned with the vibrational spectra (between 1600 cm^{-1} and 670 cm^{-1}) of para-disubstituted benzene derivatives. Jakobsen and Brewer[123] specifically discussed the spectra of para-substituted phenols in the range between 1600 cm^{-1} and 300 cm^{-1}. Bogomolov[31] discussed the characteristic vibrations of 1,2,3-substituted benzene derivatives. Jakobsen[122] studied the assignments of bands in the CsBr region (650 cm^{-1} through 250 cm^{-1}) for a large number of aromatic compounds.

Table 8 shows the vibrational modes of out-of-plane bending vibrations below 700 cm^{-1} for differently substituted benzene derivatives according to Shimanouchi et al.[299] For each type of substitution, the point group for the symmetry of the molecular skeleton is given. The numbers in the rings are the frequencies of the respective vibrations calculated under the assumption of infinitely heavy substituents (solid circles). The exact figures for the calculated displacement vectors are given in the original publication.

Bands of benzene derivatives in the range below about 700 cm^{-1} are mainly due to bending vibrations of the aromatic system. The in-plane ring bending vibrations generally occur 100 to 200 cm^{-1} higher than the

TABLE 8. Calculated Frequencies of Out-of-Plane Ring Bending Vibrations Below 700 cm^{-1} for Differently Substituted Benzene Derivatives*

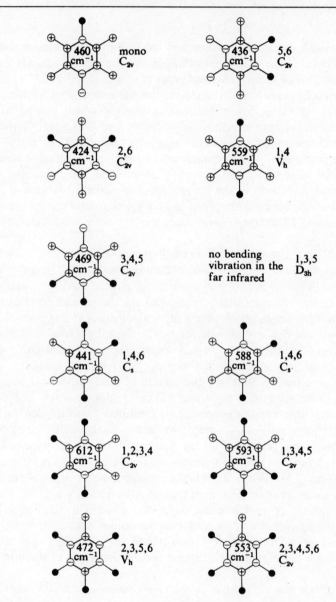

* According to Shimanouchi *et al.*[299] The substituents are considered fixed (infinite mass).

out-of-plane ring bending vibrations. At least in the case of mono-substituted and disubstituted benzene derivatives the out-of-plane ring deformations are more intense than the in-plane vibrations. Also, the former ones are influenced by the type of substituent (see Table 10, according to Jakobsen[122]).

The out-of-plane bending vibrations of aromatic-bound hydrogen atoms usually occur between 700 cm^{-1} and 900 cm^{-1}. Only in some cases hydrogen γ-vibrations may be found between about 650 cm^{-1} and 700 cm^{-1}.

Substituents on the aromatic ring system may also show in-plane and out-of-plane bending vibrations, sometimes called δ- and γ-vibrations, respectively. For substituents other than hydrogen, Jakobsen[122] gives the ranges 220–410 cm^{-1} (in-plane) and 135–250 cm^{-1} (out-of-plane) for monosubstituted benzene derivatives; and 200–460 cm^{-1} (in-plane) and 140–370 cm^{-1} (out-of-plane) for para-disubstituted benzene derivatives.

Table 9 shows the variation of the frequency of infrared-active ring deformation vibrations with the type of substitution, according to Jakobsen.[122] The ranges for the out-of-plane ring bending vibrations of differently substituted compounds sometimes differ considerably from

TABLE 9. Variation of Infrared-Active Ring Deformation Vibrations with the type of Substitution, according to Jakobsen[122]

Number of substituents	Ring position	Frequency range (cm^{-1})	Vibrational mode (a)	Intensity (b)
Mono-	1	605–625	δ	mw–m
		418–560	γ	ms–s
Di-	1,2	495–555	δ	w–m
		418–470	γ	ms–s
	1,3	505–560	δ	m–ms
		415–490	γ	ms–s
	1,4	615–650	δ	w–m
		446–552	γ	ms–s
Tri-	1,2,4	428–476	γ	m–s
	1,3,5	500–535	?	s
		450–470	?	m
	1,2,3	535–570	γ	s
Tetra-	1,2,3,4	568–585	?	ms–s
	1,2,3,5	505–580	γ	m–ms
	1,2,4,5	420–470	?	ms–s
Penta-	1,2,3,4,5	558–580	?	s
Hexa-	1,2,3,4,5,6	385–415	?	m–s

(a) δ: in-plane ring deformation; γ: out-of-plane ring deformation.
(b) Symbols: w = weak; m = medium; s = strong.

the values calculated by Shimanouchi *et al.*[299] This is probably due to the sensitivity of the out-of-plane force constants to the polarity of the substituent. The effect of this sensitivity is shown in Table 10 where the positions for the out-of-plane ring bending vibration for different types of substituents are given.

TABLE 10. Position of the Out-of-Plane Ring Deformation Vibration for Monosubstituted Benzene Derivatives According to Jakobsen[122]

Substituents	Position
$\diagup C = C \diagdown$, $-C \equiv C-$, $-C \equiv N$	near 550 cm^{-1}
electron donors: $-OH$, $-NH_2$	near 500 cm^{-1}
electron acceptors: $-COOH$, $-NO_2$	below 450 cm^{-1}

2. POLYSTYRENE

Monomer unit:

Conventional polystyrene is obtained by a radical process usually in a suspension or emulsion system. It is an amorphous and probably atactic polymer with no preferred configuration of the asymmetric carbon atoms in the vinyl chain.

The vibrational spectrum of polystyrene was studied by a large number of authors. The first figures on the Raman spectrum of polystyrene were given by Signer and Weiler[305]; a more complete Raman spectrum was published later by Palm[244]. Thompson and Torkington[335], for the first time, discussed the infrared spectrum of polystyrene. A more thorough study of the infrared and Raman spectrum of conventional amorphous polystyrene was published by Liang and Krimm[166]. Their results on the far infrared absorptions, together with ours, are shown in Table 11. The approximate normal modes of the monosubstituted benzene ring in the far infrared, according to Liang and Krimm, are depicted in Table 12. Figure 18 shows the far infrared absorptions of conventional polystyrene sheets. Pfann *et al.*[248] and Kämmerer *et al.*[129] published infrared spectroscopic methods for the determination of end groups in polystyrene.

Of the seven infrared absorptions of atactic polystyrene below 700 cm^{-1} four are in-plane and out-of-plane deformation vibrations of the aromatic

Atactic polystyrene			Isotactic polystyrene (prepared with Ziegler catalysts)					
			Takeda et al.[331]			Tadokoro et al[327]		This report[115]
Liang and Krimm[166] (cm^{-1})	Tadokoro et al.[327] (cm^{-1})	This report (cm^{-1})	Crystalline (cm^{-1})	Solution (cm^{-1})	Molten (cm^{-1})	Quenched (cm^{-1})	Crystalline (cm^{-1})	Crystalline (cm^{-1})
670		677						
622	620	618	620		620	620	620	620
			587			590	586	588
		~ 565 (sh)	567	560			566	565
	557							
					552		550	550
542	542	536						
			499				499	498
			465*					
446		440						
			426				429	422
410		402						
325		320						
216								

Symbol: sh = shoulder.
* This band, according to Takeda et al.[331] is not present in an isotactic polystyrene prepared with Al(C$_2$H$_5$)$_3$–TiCl$_3$.

ring (Liang and Krimm[166]). The weak bands at 446 cm^{-1} and 325 cm^{-1} were assigned to chain bending vibrations. The assignment of the band at about 460 cm^{-1} is dubious. This band was not found by Tadokoro et al.[327] and is not found in the spectrum of isotactic polystyrene. The assignment by Liang and Krimm[166] of the band at 216 cm^{-1} shown in Table 12 disagrees with the calculated value of 460 cm^{-1} for this vibration mode shown in Table 8. The assignments given in Table 12, therefore, may be subject to correction.

TABLE 12. Approximate Normal Modes of Monosubstituted Benzene Ring in the Far Infrared According to Liang and Krimm[166]

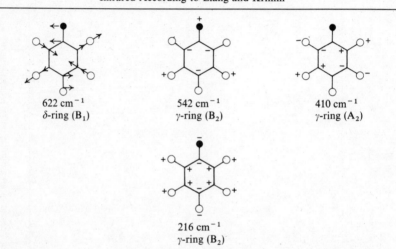

Isotactic polystyrene was first described by Natta and Corradini[221]. It is formed during the polymerization of styrene by stereospecific catalysts of the Ziegler type and can be isolated from the crude polymer as an ether-insoluble matter. It is highly crystalline, has a molecular weight of 10^5–10^6, and a first order transition temperature of about 210°C. The x-ray density of the crystallites is 1.124. The unit cell is similar to that of isotactic polypropylene. It contains two chain sequences parallel to the chain axes with three monomer units per repeat. The conformation of the chains is helical with three monomer units in a coil as in the helix of isotactic polypropylene. A crystallizable polystyrene, prepared by "Alfin" catalysts, is probably also isotactic (Takeda et al.[331]). The infrared spectrum of isotactic polystyrene (see Figure 19) was studied by a large number of authors (Tadokoro et al.[327], Takeda et al.[331], Braun et al.[34],

Morero et al.[207], Natta et al.[223], Onishi and Krimm[241], and Hummel and Busse[115]). The spectra of deuterated isotactic and atactic polystyrenes were studied by Tadokoro et al.[327], and Onishi and Krimm[241]. The spectrum of isotactic, crystalline, or amorphous polystyrene is distinctly different from the spectrum of atactic polystyrene.

Tadokoro et al.[327, 328] were the first who could show that bands in the crystalline material at 1363, 1314, 1297, and 1185 cm^{-1} (7.33, 7.61, 7.71, and 8.44 μ) belong to CH_2 and CH-wagging and twisting vibrations, and very likely are connected with the helical conformation of the chains. This assignment is supported by the observation that similar bands at 1358, 1304, and 1167 cm^{-1} are found in the spectrum of crystalline, isotactic polypropylene. The strongest evidence for this assignment is given by the fact that similar bands can be observed also in the spectra of isotactic and ring-substituted (methyl, deuterium) polystyrenes, but not in chain-deuterated isotactic polystyrenes (see also Murahashi et al.[211]). Since in the case of quenched isotactic polystyrene these bands are weaker but still observable, it is concluded that amorphous isotactic polystyrene at least partially retains the helical structure. Also, these bands remain in the spectrum of dissolved (CS_2) isotactic polystyrene. Hence, it seems reasonable to assume that the helices essentially remain intact also in solution.* (As to the discussion of three different types of bands sensitive to changes in configuration, conformation, and crystallinity, see also Takeda et al.[331], and Onishi and Krimm[241].)

A second group of bands, including five in the far infrared range, do not occur in the spectrum of atactic polystyrene. However, they can be observed only in crystalline isotactic polystyrene and disappear upon melting or dissolving of the material. They are very likely connected with far reaching intra- and intermolecular interactions in the crystalline material. The maxima of the bands are at 984, 923, 901, 620, 587, 499, 465, and 426 cm^{-1} (10.16, 10.83, 11.10, 16.13, 17.04, 20.04, 21.5, and 23.5 μ). Especially useful for the determination of crystallinity are the bands at 984 cm^{-1} and 499 cm^{-1} (Braun[34], Hummel and Busse[115]).

The doublet at 1085 cm^{-1} and 1054 cm^{-1} as well as the asymmetric band at 567 cm^{-1} are vibrations of the phenyl group and form a third group of bands (Takeda et al.[331]). They are sensitive against the short-range order within a chain, i.e. the alternating *trans–gauche* conformation in the isotactic sequences, and all-*trans* conformation in syndiotactic sequences. The band at about 565 cm^{-1} (the figures given for this band differ slightly in the different papers) is very likely characteristic for *trans–*

---

* This cannot be generalized. Schmidt[285] for instance concluded from his experimental results that amorphous isotactic polypropylene has a non-helical conformation.

gauche sequences. Takeda *et al.*[331] suggest the ratio of the absorbances A_{560}/A_{543} as a measure for isotactic sequences.

The observation of this group of bands characteristic for short range order in stereoregular polymers is of basic interest since one and three-dimensional crystallinity are derived magnitudes, and consequently not in all instances a measure of the content of a polymer in eutactic configurations.

3. COPOLYMERS OF STYRENE

"Zerlon 150" is a copolymer of about equal parts of styrene with methyl methacrylate. In its far infrared spectrum (Figure 20), the bands of both monomer units can be observed. However, the intense doublet of polystyrene near 540 cm^{-1} is fused to a single band with its maximum at 550 cm^{-1}. Styrene–butadiene copolymers are an example of styrene copolymers where only the styrene component can be detected in the far infrared.

4. POLY-α-METHYLSTYRENE

Bentley and Wolfarth[23], in their publication on the analytical applications of far infrared spectra, studied a number of alkyl-substituted benzene derivatives. From their spectra of monosubstituted alkylbenzenes, it is evident that the strong band in the range of about 18–21.5 μ (555–465 cm^{-1}) is very sensitive to α-branching of the substituent. Normal alkylbenzenes and isoalkylbenzenes with the branching not in α-position show this band around 500 cm^{-1}. A branching in α-position shifts this band to about 550 cm^{-1} whereas a second branch in α-position apparently has only a slight influence on the position of this band. The values for isobutylbenzene, s-butylbenzene, and t-butylbenzene are 496 cm^{-1}, 543, and 537 cm^{-1} (doublet), and 544 cm^{-1}, respectively.

The same observation can be made with polystyrene and poly-α-methylstyrene. The former absorbs at 536 cm^{-1} (Figure 18) the latter at 547 cm^{-1} (Figure 21). However, the band of polystyrene is, as in the case of isobutylbenzene, an unresolved doublet, whereas the band of poly-α-methylstyrene is a single, almost symmetrical band as in the spectrum of t-butylbenzene.

In this connection, it has to be mentioned that Jakobsen[122] assigns a band near 540 cm^{-1} in the spectra of alkylbenzenes to a C—C—C bending vibration of the substituent, whereas Liang and Krimm[166] assigned this band in polystyrene to an out-of-plane ring bending vibration (see Table 12).

5. RING-SUBSTITUTED POLYSTYRENES

Ring-substituted styrenes, as styrene itself, can be polymerized with stereospecific catalysts. The resulting polymers are amorphous and crystallize only with difficulty (Murahashi et al.[211]). However, they have an isotactic and helical structure similar to that of isotactic polystyrene. This is evidenced by the appearance of bands assigned to the helical vinyl chain, 1361, 1314, and 1290 cm^{-1} for poly-p-methylstyrene, and 1361, 1310, and 1190 cm^{-1} for poly-m-methylstyrene (Tadokoro et al.[328]). Another support for the isotactic and helical structure of these ring-substituted polystyrenes, prepared with Ziegler catalysts, is the observation of Natta et al.[223] that isotactic polystyrene and poly-p-methylstyrene are isomorphous. The far infrared spectra of these polymers are not published as yet. Quantitative measurements on p-substituted polystyrenes were reported by Hummel and Lünebach[116].

The atactic ring-substituted derivatives of polystyrene have had industrial interest. The strongest band in the far infrared spectrum of atactic poly-p-methylstyrene (Figure 22) is a doublet with maxima at about 553 cm^{-1} and 530 cm^{-1}. The position of the former agrees well with the frequency calculated for an out-of-plane bending vibration of 1,4-substituted benzene derivatives of the point group V_h by Shimanouchi et al.[299] (Table 8). In the far infrared spectrum of poly-p-isopropylstyrene (Figure 23), the maximum of this band is shifted to about 580 cm^{-1}. A technical copolymer of vinyltoluene (mixture of isomers) and acrylonitrile was Cymac 201 (Figure 24).

6. POLYINDENE

The olefinic double bond of indene is fairly reactive. Hence, indene can be polymerized with Lewis and other acids. Polyindenes of technical grade are resins with a rather low molecular weight; they are used as chemically resistant components in surface coatings. The monomer unit in polyindenes

contains two pseudo-asymmetric carbon atoms. Furthermore, the addition may happen in head-to-tail or head-to-head and tail-to-tail fashion. Consequently, a number of different stereoregular polymers is theoretically possible. To date, nothing has been published about stereoregular polyindenes. The infrared spectra of technical polyindenes were reported by Brause and Heinze[35] and by Eckardt and Heinze[68].

The far infrared spectrum of a technical polyindene (Figure 25) is characterized by a fairly strong band at about 420 cm^{-1}. This agrees rather well with the value (436 cm^{-1}) calculated by Shimanouchi *et al.*[299] for an out-of-plane bending vibration of *o*-substituted benzene derivatives (see Table 8).

C. Halogenated Polyhydrocarbons (Chart III)

1. CHLORINATED POLYHYDROCARBONS

It has been generally observed that certain vibrations in a molecule are sensitive to the conformation of the vibrational group with respect to a neighboring group. Thus, the C—X stretching vibration in 1-substituted alkanes is sensitive to the position of the substituent X with respect to the C-atom in β position. In vinyl polymers of the general formula

$$(-CH-CH_2)_n,$$
$$\quad | $$
$$\quad X$$

the C—X stretching vibration is sensitive to the conformation of the C—C chain within certain distances of the C—X group.

The ` carbon–halogen stretching vibrations in alkyl halides received considerable attention since they are easily detectable and rather sensitive to the conformation in the chain. According to Brown and Sheppard[37], the 1,2-dihalogen ethanes have two spectroscopically distinguishable rotational isomers, namely, a *trans*-form where the two halogens are in a *trans*-position, and a *gauche*-form where the two halogens are at an angle of 60° to each other with respect to the C—C bond.

Trimethylene halides have four spectroscopically distinguishable rotational isomers, namely, those in *trans–trans*, *trans–gauche*, and in two different *gauche–gauche* conformations. As the methylene chain between the chlorine atoms becomes large, the number of possible rotational isomers increases. However, these isomers finally become indistinguishable by infrared spectroscopic methods. Other carbon–halogen compounds were investigated by Sheppard[295], Mizushima *et al.*[205], Nakagawa and Mizushima[212], and Komaki *et al.*[143].

Shimanouchi and his coworkers[302] proposed a rule concerning the spectral regions of various C—Cl stretching vibrations. According to this, the C—Cl stretching band of secondary chlorides with Cl *trans* to H is expected between 600 cm^{-1} and 640 cm^{-1}; the C—Cl stretching band with Cl *trans* to C is expected between 670 cm^{-1} and 700 cm^{-1}.

These considerations can be transferred to vinyl polymers, especially to the polyvinyl halides and similar compounds. However, every second carbon atom in polyvinyl halides is pseudo-asymmetric, and the configuration of the substituents at these carbon atoms may be either d or l. The possible chain conformations in polyvinyl halides therefore depend on the configuration at the asymmetric carbon atoms. This shall be discussed for polyvinyl chlorides of a different structure.

a. *Polyvinyl Chloride*

Conventional polyvinyl chloride is obtained by an emulsion or dispersion polymerization and with radical catalysts. Dehalogenation with metallic zinc yields a polymer with cyclopropane groups (Marvel et al.[182] and Hodgkins[107]); this is chemical proof for the head-to-tail structure of polyvinyl chloride. Conventional polyvinyl chloride is not crystallizable. The pseudo-asymmetric carbon atoms in its vinyl chain seem to have a somewhat prevailing d,l-configuration according to a syndiotactic chain.

The infrared spectrum of polyvinyl chloride was studied by a large number of authors. The more recent publications were contributed by Krimm and his collaborators[153-156], Grisenthwaite and Hunter[93], Fordham et al.[76] (low-temperature polymers), Narita et al.[215], Kawasaki et al.[136, 138], Shimanouchi et al.[301, 302], Enomoto and Asahina[70], Asahina and Enomoto[7], Iimura and Takeda[117], Tasumi and Shimanouchi[332] and Takeda and Iimura[330], Bailey et al.[10] prepared head-to-head polyvinyl chloride and examined its infrared spectrum. Stromberg et al.[318] observed band shifts in the spectrum of thermally degraded polyvinyl chloride.

Polymerization at low temperatures seems to favor the formation of syndiotactic chains. There are also some catalyst systems with a certain degree of stereospecificity which preferably form syndiotactic and crystallizable polyvinyl chloride. Kawasaki et al.[136] used a mixture of aluminum triethyl and di-t-butylperoxide at room temperature, and a mixture of boron triethyl and cumene hydroperoxide at $-65°C$. Takeda and Iimura[330] used a mixture of boron triisobutyl and azodiisobutyronitrile as a catalyst. The radiation-initiated polymerization of vinyl chloride–urea complexes at low temperatures also yields crystallizable polymers with a high degree of syndiotacticity (Shimanouchi et al.[301, 302], Krimm et al.[153]).

Samples with different density, and probably also with different crystallinity, were studied by Kawasaki et al.[136, 138]. The authors found absorptions increasing with the density of a sample at 1428, 1333, 1254, 1226, and 961 cm^{-1} (7.00, 7.50, 7.98, 8.15, and 10.41 μ).

The assignment of the four C—Cl stretching vibrations* between 600 cm^{-1} and 700 cm^{-1} (690, 638, 615, and 603 cm^{-1}) for some time was a subject of controversy between different groups of spectroscopists. If we take into consideration the conformation of only two adjacent monomer units, then the first, and probably most complex absorption (680–690 cm^{-1}) is in the range for conformations with Cl *trans* to C; the three others are in the range for conformations with Cl *trans* to H. These conformations are possible for certain structures in both isotactic and syndiotactic sequences.

Very instructive are studies of Shimanouchi and Tasumi[300] with stereoregular 2,4-dichloropentanes. Table 13 shows the possible rotational isomers of *meso-* and *dl*-2,4-dichloropentanes. Applying the rule of

TABLE 13. Possible Rotational Isomers of *Meso-* and *dl*-2,4-Dichloropentanes according to Shimanouchi and Tasumi[300]

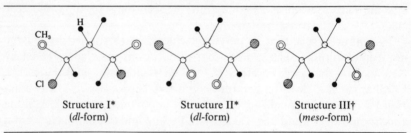

Structure I*   Structure II*   Structure III†
(*dl*-form)   (*dl*-form)   (*meso*-form)

* Model compound for syndiotactic polyvinyl chloride.
† Model compound for isotactic polyvinyl chloride.

Shimanouchi *et al.*[206, 302], we can expect two bands in the range 600–640 cm^{-1} (Cl *trans* to H) for structure I, two bands between 670 cm^{-1} and 700 cm^{-1} (Cl *trans* to C) for structure II, and one band in each of the two ranges for structure III (in structure III one Cl is *trans* to H and one Cl *trans* to C). Table 14 shows the far infrared absorptions of the different 2,4-dichloropentanes. Apparently the *dl*-form has the structure I and the *meso*-form, the structure III.

In fact, *dl*-2,4-dichloropentane is a model compound for syndiotactic polyvinyl chloride and *meso*-2,4-dichloropentane is a model compound for isotactic polyvinyl chloride. The two C—Cl bands observed in the spectrum of *dl*-2,4-dichloropentane correspond to the bands at 638 cm^{-1}

* It is noteworthy that these four bands are to some extent sensitive to deuteration of the chain. They are, therefore, not pure C—Cl stretching vibrations but couple with chain vibrations.

and 603 cm^{-1} found in crystalline, syndiotactic polyvinyl chloride. The only possible structure for a chain of this type with Cl *trans* to H is an extended syndiotactic one.

TABLE 14. Far Infrared Absorptions of 2,4-Dichloropentanes

Compound	Phase	Wavenumber (cm^{-1})	
dl-2,4-Dichloropentane	Gaseous	645	622
	Liquid	631	610
	Solid	623	597
meso-2,4-Dichloropentane	Liquid	683	619

The band at 690 cm^{-1} belongs to a conformation Cl *trans* to C. The *dl*-2,4-dichloropentane showed no band near 690 cm^{-1} but the *meso*-form did. Consequently, it is very likely that the band near 690 cm^{-1} in conventional polyvinyl chloride belongs to isotactic sequences, probably in a

TABLE 15. Far Infrared Bands of Polyvinyl Chloride*

Wavenumber, cm^{-1}	Dichroic behavior	Relative intensity	Phase†	Assignment‡
693	‖			
685	⊥	m	A	ν (CCl) S_{HC} (A)
640	⊥	ms	C	ν (CCl) A_1
~638	⊥	ms	A	ν (CCl) S'_{HH} (A)
615	⊥	s	A	ν (CCl) S_{HH} (A)
604	⊥‖§	s	C	ν (CCl) B_1
588	⊥	vw (sh)	A	ν (CCl) T_{HHC}
570		vw (sh)	C	
540	‖	vw	A	ν (CCl) T_{HHH}
492	‖	vw	C	skeleton vibration
427	‖ ?	vw	A	δ (CCl)
418	not determ.	vw	C	
363	not determ.	w		δ (CCl)
315	not determ.	vw (sh)		γ_w (CCl)
182	not determ.	w		skeleton vibration
160	not determ.	w		skeleton vibration
102	not determ.	vw		chain rotation

* Selected from the results of several authors.
† A: amorphous; C: crystalline.
‡ Assignments according to Krimm et al.[155,156]
    S: secondary Cl (CHCl), C—C—C planar.
    S′: secondary Cl (CHCl), bent C—C—C skeleton.
    HH: Cl *trans* to H on both sides.
    HC: Cl *trans* to H on one side, and *trans* to C on the other side.
    CC: Cl *trans* to C on both sides.
    T: tertiary Cl (CCl).
§ Inversion of dichroism with drawing.

helical conformation. The possible conformations in conventional poly-vinyl chloride are shown in Table 16.

Recently Krimm and his collaborators[154] published a very thorough study on the infrared spectra and assignments for polyvinyl chloride and

TABLE 16. Possible Formations of Polymer Chains in Conventional Polyvinyl Chloride*

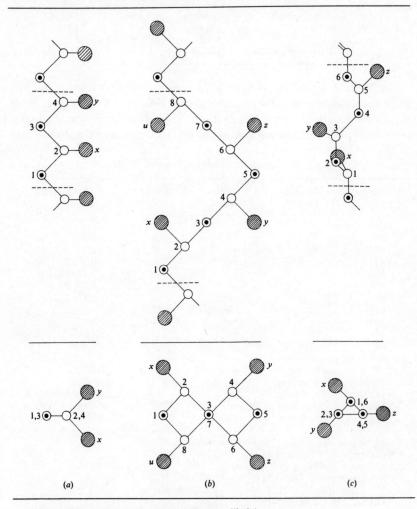

(a) extended syndiotactic structure (all-*trans*; likely).
(b) folded syndiotactic structure (-*trans–trans–gauche–gauche*-; unlikely).
(c) threefold isotactic helix (-*trans–gauche–trans–gauche*-; likely).
* T. Shimanouchi and M. Tasumi[300].

for different deuterated analogs. The authors observed that the C—Cl stretching vibrations in their frequencies depend on the conformation of the substituents on both sides of the C—Cl bond. There is also evidence that the C—Cl frequency with Cl *trans* to H on both sides depends on the conformation of the local skeleton in the vicinity of the C—Cl bond. The assignments in Table 15 are based upon these observations. Weak bands at 540 cm^{-1} and 588 cm^{-1} were associated with tertiary Cl stretching modes.

Figure 26 shows the absorptions of a sheet of conventional polyvinyl chloride. The bands at 615 cm^{-1} and 603 cm^{-1} cannot be resolved without the application of polarized infrared.

Vinyl chloride–vinyl acetate copolymers are widely used in coatings and cements. The content in vinyl acetate units makes the polymers more soluble in the usual solvents for lacquers. The far infrared spectrum of a copolymer with about 15% vinyl acetate (Figure 27) is very similar to that of a pure polyvinyl chloride. This is mainly due to the fact that the strongest band of polyvinyl acetate near 605 cm^{-1} is masked by the much stronger band of polyvinyl chloride near 615 cm^{-1}. Copolymers of this type, however, can readily be identified by their infrared spectrum in the rocksalt range.

b. *Polyvinylidene Chloride*

Vinylidene chloride polymerizes with radical catalysts to yield a polymer which is practically insoluble in most of the conventional solvents. For industrial use, it is therefore copolymerized with about 15% vinyl chloride. These copolymers, known as "Saran" (Figure 28) and others, are readily soluble in a number of solvents. The anionic polymerization and copolymerization of vinylidene chloride under the influence of *n*-butyllithium was described by Konishi[144] (more literature is given in this publication).

The identity period of the chain axis, according to x-ray examination, is rather short, namely 4.7 Å. This is more than one monomer unit but less than two for a planar zigzag. Two possible structures were suggested for this repeating period, both containing two monomer units, one by Fuller[81], the other by Reinhardt.[266] In both structures the carbon skeleton is folded.

The infrared spectra of polyvinylidene chloride and, preferably, vinylidene chloride–vinyl chloride copolymers were studied by a number of authors (Thompson and Torkington[336], Krimm and Liang[156], and Narita *et al.*[216, 217, 218]). Table 17 shows the far infrared absorptions of a vinylidene chloride–vinyl chloride copolymer with a low content of vinyl chloride. The only absorptions belonging to the vinyl chloride units or to the copolymer are the bands at 1206 cm^{-1} and 868 cm^{-1} (8.29 μ and 11.52 μ). A weak band found by Krimm and Liang[156] near 307 cm^{-1} was not observed in our spectrum.

TABLE 17. Far Infrared Absorptions of Polyvinylidene Chloride

Krimm and Liang[156] (Copolymer with a small amount of vinyl chloride) Wavenumber (cm^{-1})	This report (Dow Saran) Wavenumber (cm^{-1})	Dichroic behavior*	Assignment*
754	749	$\perp$	$\nu_a(CCl_2)_o$ (A')
657	654	$\perp$	$\nu_a(CCl_2)_i$ (A')
603	598	$\perp$	$\nu_s(CCl_2)_o$ (A')
565	563–555		?
530	528	$\perp$	$\nu_s(CCl_2)_i$ (A')
454	449	$\parallel$	$\gamma_t(CCl_2)_i$ (A'') ?; skeletal ?
430	430	$\parallel$	$\gamma_t(CCl_2)_o$ (A'') ?; skeletal ?
359	354	$\parallel$	$\gamma_w(CCl_2)_i$ (A'')
307	—	—	$\gamma_r(CCl_2)_o$ (A')
291	approx. 280	—	$\gamma_r(CCl_2)_i$ (A')
245	—	—	$\delta(CCl_2)_i$ (A')
185	—	—	skeletal ?
113	—	—	skeletal ?
102	—	—	skeletal ?

* According to Krimm and Liang[156]

The assignment of the bands at 754, 657, 603, and 530 cm^{-1} to CCl_2 stretching modes, supported by deuteration studies,* and their dichroic behavior is essential to the choice of the correct structure. Due to the two monomer units in the repeating unit and the phase relations between them, the fundamental vibrations of the CCl_2 group are doubled. As Krimm and Liang pointed out, two rather strong perpendicular bands, a weaker parallel band, and an almost inactive band should be characteristic for the Reinhardt[266] structure. On the other hand, the Fuller[81] structure implies four perpendicular bands, two of them stronger than the other two. The experimental results strongly support the Fuller[81] structure.

Polyvinylidene chloride is crystallizable. According to Narita et al.[216], the bands at 884, 753, 655, 600, 565, 527, and 450 cm^{-1} are much weaker in molten samples. Actually, the long wavelength vibrations almost fuse together into a very broad and poorly structured band. This indicates a basic change in the structure of the polymer during melting.

* As in the case of polyvinyl chloride, the CCl stretching vibrations couple quite considerably with skeleton vibrations.

Quenched samples recrystallize slowly at room temperature. This can be followed by changes in the far infrared spectrum. Stretching speeds up the rate of recrystallization.

c. *Other Chlorinated Polyhydrocarbons*

Enjay chlorobutyl is a low-chlorinated butyl rubber. The bands in its far infrared spectrum (Figure 29) are weak; the one near 670 cm^{-1} may be a C—Cl stretching vibration. The spectrum as a whole differs little from the spectrum of butyl rubber.

Chlorinated and chlorosulfonated polyethylenes obtained considerable industrial interest as components in surface coatings and synthetic rubbers. Canterino and Kahle[45] recently published a rather thorough study on the properties of chlorinated and chlorosulfonated high-density and low-density polyethylenes and ethylene–α-olefin copolymers.

The far infrared spectrum of a chlorinated high-pressure (low-density) polyethylene (Figure 30) shows rather strong bands near 660 cm^{-1} and 610 cm^{-1}. Both must be C—Cl stretching vibrations for groups with different conformation. The latter band belongs to conformations with Cl *trans* to H, the former probably to conformations Cl *trans* to C.

The infrared spectrum of chlorosulfonated polyethylene was described by Smook *et al.*[311] Its far infrared spectrum (Figure 31) has the same C—Cl bands as chlorinated polyethylene. Additional bands near 590, 565, and 533 cm^{-1} can possibly be connected with the SO$_2$Cl groups. This spectral behavior is consistent with the structure. Chlorosulfonated polyethylene contains 26–29% chlorine and only 1.3–1.7% sulfur. Consequently, the chlorine in its major part is bound directly to the chain as in chlorinated polyethylene.

1,4-Polyisoprene adds hydrogen chloride to its olefinic double bonds; according to Markovnikov's rule, the chlorine is added to the carbon atom with the smaller number of hydrogen atoms:

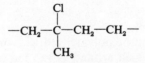

Checkland and Davison[47] described the infrared spectrum of hydrochlorinated Hevea rubber. Its far infrared spectrum (Figure 32) shows some similarity to the spectrum of conventional polyvinyl chloride (Figure 26). Bands at 743 cm^{-1} and 640 cm^{-1} were assigned to C—Cl stretching vibrations of groups where Cl is *trans* or *gauche* to the CH$_2$ group.

The chlorination of Hevea rubber not only leads to an addition of chlorine to the olefinic double bond but also to substitution reactions. The infrared spectrum of chlorinated rubber was studied by a number of authors (Allirot and Orsini[3], Salomon and van der Schee[275], and Ramakrishnan et al.[260, 261]). Its far infrared spectrum (Figure 23) differs significantly from that of hydrochlorinated rubber or polyvinyl chloride. Due to the irregular structure of chlorinated rubber and the many possible conformations of the chain, comments on the far infrared spectrum were not attempted.

The infrared spectrum of after-chlorinated polyvinyl chloride was studied by Fuchs and Louis[80]. The far infrared spectrum of chlorinated polyvinyl chloride (not shown in this collection) is characterized by the following absorptions: 682 (strong), 620 (medium), 555 (very weak), 487 (weak), and 400 cm^{-1} (strong). The polymer can be easily differentiated from polyvinyl chloride itself by the reverse intensity of the absorptions near 680 cm^{-1} and 620 cm^{-1}.

2. FLUORINATED POLYHYDROCARBONS, POLYFLUOROCARBONS, AND POLY(CHLOROFLUOROCARBONS)

a. Polyvinyl Fluoride

Vinyl fluoride polymerizes with radical catalysts at high pressures to form a polymer with a melting range of 170–190°C and a density of 1.30 g cm^{-3}. A polymerization process was described by Kalb et al.[127] Polyvinyl fluoride ("Teslar") is used for chemically resistant surface coatings and for films.

The strong bands in its far infrared spectrum (Figure 34) are mainly due to deformation vibrations involving the CHF group. Since they are weaker than the extremely strong CF-stretching vibrations in the range of 1100 cm^{-1}, the conventional films with thicknesses around 30–50 μ can easily be studied in the far infrared but not in the rocksalt range.

b. Polyvinylidene Fluoride

Vinylidene fluoride can be polymerized with radical catalysts (McBee et al.[179]). The polymers melt around 170°C and have a density of 1.76 g cm^{-3}. The technical product is called "Kynar."

The far infrared absorptions of polyvinylidene fluoride (Figure 35) mainly stem from deformation vibrations of the CF_2 group. As already mentioned for polyvinyl fluoride, the stretching vibrations in the rocksalt range are extremely strong. Hence the far infrared range is more suitable for the identification of films with the usual thicknesses around 30–50 μ.

c. *Polytetrafluoroethylene*

Polytetrafluoroethylene is a highly crystalline material with a density of 2.2 g cm^{-3} and a transition temperature of 327°C. However, the material does not really melt at this temperature but only becomes amorphous and plastic.

According to x-ray studies of Bunn and Howells[41], a polymer chain in crystalline polytetrafluoroethylene consists of a helical arrangement of 13 CF_2 groups in the identity period. There is a phase transition at 19°C which seems to be accompanied by a change in the identity period, there now being 15 CF_2 groups in the repeat.

The infrared spectrum of the polymer was investigated by a number of authors (Liang and Krimm[166], Moynihan[210], Bro and Sperati[36], Robinson and Price[270], Pokrovsky and Kotova[251,252], and Miller and Willis[192]). The far infrared bands and their assignments given by Krimm[151], together with those found through this study, are shown in Table 18. It is interesting to note the parallelism between the infrared

TABLE 18. Far Infrared Absorptions of Polytetrafluoroethylene

Krimm[151]	This report	Dichroic behavior	Assignment
Wavenumber (cm^{-1})			
740	738	‖	Not determined
720	717	‖	Not determined
703	700 (sh)	Not determined	Not determined
—	670 (sh)	Not determined	Not determined
638	638	‖	$\gamma_w(CF_2) (A_2)_{13}$
625	625	‖	$\gamma_w(CF_2) (A_2)_{15}$
553	554	⊥	$\delta(CF_2) (F_1)$
516	515	‖	$\gamma_t(CF_2) (A_2)$
384	380–385	‖	Not determined
321	*	Not determined	$\gamma_t(CF_2) (F_1)$
277	*	Not determined	$\gamma_w(CF_2) (E_1)$
203	—		$\gamma_r(CF_2) (E_1)$
149	—	Not determined	Not determined
124	—	Not determined	Not determined
102	—	Not determined	Not determined

* Not observed due to strong water bands. Symbol: sh = shoulder.

spectra of polyethylene (Figure 3) with the structure $(CH_2—)_n$, and that of polytetrafluoroethylene with the structure $(CF_2—)_n$ (Figure 36). However, according to the assignment of Krimm the CF_2-bending vibration has a lower frequency than the CF_2-wagging frequency. Generally, the intramolecular forces in the $(CF_2—)_n$ chain are much stronger than in the polyethylene chain. This is also expressed by the fact that a minor change in the structure, namely the rearrangement of the thirteen-fold helix to a fifteen-fold helix, can be noticed by a shift of the CF_2-wagging vibration from 638 cm^{-1} to 625 cm^{-1}. In cases of weaker intra- or intermolecular forces, enantiomorphous modifications may have the same infrared spectrum.

Infrared methods for the determination of crystallinity in polytetrafluoroethylene were described by Pokrovsky and Kotova[252], and by Miller and Willis[192]. A method for the determination of end groups in polytetrafluoroethylene was described by Bro and Sperati[36].

d. *Polychlorotrifluoroethylene*

Polychlorotrifluoroethylene is highly crystalline and differs from polytetrafluoroethylene by melting at about 300°C without decomposition. Its structure is not yet fully understood. It is assumed that polychlorotrifluoroethylene is stereoregular and has a helical structure.

The infrared spectrum of the polymer was studied by Liang and Krimm[166]. Their figures and assignments, together with ours (Figure 37), are shown in Table 19. Iwasaki *et al.*[120] studied the decomposition of

TABLE 19. Far Infrared Absorptions of Polychlorotrifluoroethylene

Liang and Krimm[166]	This report	Dichroic behavior	Assignment
Wavenumber (cm^{-1})			
—	689	Not determined	—
658	666	‖	—
580	589	‖	CF_2-wagging (A)
(535)	530 (sh)	?	—
506	501	⊥ ?	CF_2-bending (E_1)
490	?	‖	CF_2-rocking (A)
438	436	‖	CClF-wagging (A)
390	385	‖ ?	—
365	—	?	—
335	330–35	unpol.	CClF-bending (E_1)
297	—	Not determined	CF_2-wagging (?) (E_1)
235	—	Not determined	CF_2-rocking (E_1)
185	—	Not determined	CClF-rocking (E_1)
102	—	Not determined	—

Symbol: sh = shoulder.

polychlorotrifluoroethylene by an infrared spectroscopic method. Hoffman and Weeks[108] and Matsuo[184, 185] determined the crystallinity of the polymer by an infrared method.

Iwasaki *et al.*[121] studied the infrared spectra of tetrafluoroethylene–trifluorochloroethylene copolymers. They found characteristic bands for different arrangements between the tetrafluoroethylene (A) and trifluorochloroethylene (B) monomer units: ABA 957 cm^{-1}, ABB 967 cm^{-1}, BBB 971 cm^{-1}.

A copolymer of chlorotrifluoroethylene and vinylidene fluoride (KEL—F 827) has a far infrared spectrum (Figure 37) very similar to that of pure polytrifluorochloroethylene (Figure 38). Only the shift of the maximum at 500 cm^{-1} to 510 cm^{-1} reveals the presence of the vinylidene fluoride unit.

D. Alkyds and Other Resinous Esters (Chart IV)

1. GENERAL REMARKS ON THE FAR INFRARED ABSORPTIONS OF ESTERS

If we consider the ester group as a plane, three-pointed star, then this "molecule" of four atoms is able to perform the following vibrations (wave-numbers in brackets for gaseous acetone):

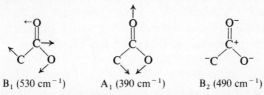

B_1 (530 cm^{-1}) A_1 (390 cm^{-1}) B_2 (490 cm^{-1})

The first one is asymmetric with respect to the C=O axis and a degenerate vibration. During this vibration all atoms of the group perform non-linear movements in the plane of the ester group. In a first approximation, the single-bonded C and O describe circles. The second one is a bending vibration symmetric to the C=O axis, the third one is an out-of-plane deformation vibration of the group. The above assignments were given by Mirone[192a] for gaseous acetone. The assignment suggested by Katon and Bentley[132] for similar vibrations of ketones is less probable than the one of Mirone.

The frequency of these vibrations strongly depends on the type of substituent since there is a strong mechanical coupling between the deformation vibrations of the ester group and deformation vibrations of the substituents. The first of these vibrations is especially sensitive to mechanical coupling and inductive effects and may be found in the region between 650 cm^{-1} and 500 cm^{-1}. Also, the intensity has been found to vary strongly. The other two bands are frequently found near 350 cm^{-1} and 450 cm^{-1}, respectively.

More detailed information on the far infrared absorptions of esters is available from a recent publication of Lucier and Bentley[177].

2. OIL-FREE ALKYD RESINS

Oil-free alkyd resins, or "glyptals," are polyesters of phthalic acid with tri- or polyvalent alcohols like glycerol or pentaerythritol. The spectral pattern in the far infrared is governed by the absorptions of the ester groups and the aromatic ring system. Different kinds of aliphatic alcohols have only a slight influence on the far infrared spectrum. All types of phthalic acid esters possess a sharp band at 650 cm^{-1} (Figure 39). This may be assigned to the degenerate bending vibration of the ester group since the highest in-plane bending vibration of the *ortho*-substituted benzene ring, according to Jacobsen[122], absorbs at lower frequencies between 495 cm^{-1} and 555 cm^{-1}. However, this assignment is not very suitable since a bending vibration of the ester group should exhibit at least some sensitivity to the kind of aliphatic substituent. Also characteristic for the ester group but less obvious are bands around 415 cm^{-1} and 350 cm^{-1}. The band near 562 cm^{-1} can possibly be assigned to the in-plane bending vibration of the aromatic ring.

Spurr *et al.*[313] studied the infrared spectrum of diallyl phthalate polymers. The far infrared spectrum of a diallyl phthalate prepolymer (Figure 40) is rather similar to that of oil-free alkyd resins.

3. OIL-MODIFIED ALKYD RESINS

Oil-modified alkyds are widely used for lacquers and paints. The ones containing a high percentage of highly unsaturated vegetable oils are air-drying. Those containing smaller percentages of oil ("short-oil" alkyds), or mainly saturated fatty acids, have to be baked at higher temperatures.

Isolated and conjugated olefinic double bonds in *trans*-configuration absorb between 980 cm^{-1} and 950 cm^{-1}. *Cis*-olefinic groups prevailing in natural oils have a broad absorption around 730 cm^{-1} which is merged with the methylene-rocking vibration at about 720 cm^{-1} of the long aliphatic chains. There is no infrared spectroscopic method for the direct determination of the *cis*-content in oils because this band is too diffuse and inseparable from the methylene-rocking vibration. Unfortunately, there seems to be no useful absorption of *cis*-vinylene groups in the far infrared either.

Oil-modified alkyd resins in their far infrared spectra (Figures 41–44) differ from the oil-free alkyds by a rather significant band at about 480 cm^{-1}. This band seems to belong to a vibration of the ester group in long-chain esters.

The far infrared absorptions of vegetable oils are generally weak. If the oils for practical purposes are modified with strongly absorbing resins like the epoxy resins, then the spectrum of this modified oil is very similar to that of the pure modifying resin. The far infrared spectrum of an epoxy-modified dehydrated castor oil (Figure 45) is very similar to that of a pure epoxy resin (Figure 93).

Oil-modified alkyd resins based on isophthalic acid differ only slightly in their far infrared spectrum (Figure 46) from the alkyd resins based on phthalic acid. Isophthalic acid polyesters normally show a pair of bands near 650 cm^{-1} where o-phthalates have a single and sharp band. The maximum of the broad band of o-phthalate alkyds near 360 cm^{-1} shifts to about 340 cm^{-1} in the spectrum of isophthalate alkyds.

4. TEREPHTHALIC ACID POLYESTERS

a. *Poly(ethylene terephthalate)*

Poly(ethylene terephthalate) was first developed by ICI on a technical scale and is now widely used as a very tough and resistant material for films (Mylar, Hostaphan) and fibers (Terylene). The monomer unit is:

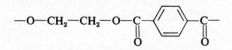

The polymer can be crystallized to a rather high percentage of crystallinity. The crystal structure was studied by x-ray diffraction by a number of authors (Daubeny et al.[59], Johnson[124], Heffelfinger and Burton[101], and Farrow *et al.*[71]). According to Daubeny *et al.*[59] the unit cell contains one monomer unit, is triclinic, and has the following dimensions: a = 4.56 Å, b = 5.94 Å, c = 10.75 Å, α = 98.5°, β = 118°, γ = 112°. This gives the density of the crystals as 1.455 g cm^{-3}. The entirely amorphous material has a density of 1.335 g cm^{-3}.

The molecules in the unit cell are nearly coplanar. The unit cell has a center of symmetry. A slight deviation from planarity results from the COO groups being about 12° out of the plane of the benzene rings. It is also thought that the CH$_2$—CH$_2$ bond is rotated about 20° around the O—CH$_2$ bond from the planar configuration.

The infrared spectrum of poly(ethylene terephthalate) is very complex due to the large number of atoms in the monomer unit, and also due to the different rotational isomers of the polymer. Earlier investigators were Miller and Willis[192], Tobin[340], Daniels and Kitson[57], and Grime and Ward[92]. Measurements of birefringence, infrared dichroism, and x-ray diffraction have been made by Dulmage and Geddes[67] on crystallized and uncrystallized poly(ethylene terephthalate) films stretched up to 500%. At high elongations, stretching induces high linear orientation of the chain molecules parallel to the direction of stretch. A comprehensive study of the infrared spectrum of oriented films of poly(ethylene terephthalate) was published by Liang and Krimm[165] and by Krimm[151]. The far infrared bands and their assignment, given in the latter paper, are reproduced in Table 20, together with our results. Figure 47 shows a commercial film of poly(ethylene terephthalate). It should be noted that there is

TABLE 20. Far Infrared Absorptions of Poly(ethylene Terephthalate)

Krimm[151]	This report	Dichroic behavior	Assignment*
Wavenumber (cm^{-1})			
680	678	⊥	$\gamma_4(B_2)$?
633	630	‖	combination
			$\gamma'_{18B} + \delta(C-O-C)$
613	610 (br)	⊥	$\gamma_{6B}(B_1)$?
575	—	‖	combination
			$\gamma_{10B} + \gamma_{16B}$
525	520 (br)	‖	$\gamma_{6A}(A_1)$
502	504	‖	$\gamma_w(C=O)$
437	?	‖	$\delta(CCO)$
430	431	⊥	$\gamma_{16B}(B_{1u})$
383	377	‖	$\delta(COC)$
355	350	⊥	$\gamma_r(C=O)$
250	Not determined	Not determined	$\gamma'_{18B}(B_{2u})$
145	Not determined	Not determined	
approx. 95	Not determined	Not determined	

Symbol: br = broad.
* For the form of the normal modes, see Liang and Krimm[165,166] and Pitzer and Scott.[250]

considerable disagreement between the band assignments of different authors: this is discussed, among others, by Tadokoro et al.[329].

A number of authors were especially interested in the effect of crystallinity on the infrared spectrum of poly(ethylene terephthalate) (Cobbs and Burton[52], Miller and Willis[192], Miyake[194], and Liang and Krimm[164]). The intensity of a relatively large number of bands is a function of the crystallinity of the specimen. Table 21 shows bands whose frequency and intensity depend on the crystallinity of a sample. There is a pronounced increase in absorptions at 1340 cm^{-1} and 972 cm^{-1} upon crystallization of the polymer. An "amorphous" band according to Miller and Willis[192] which is not sensitive to the orientation of the sample is the medium absorption near 898 cm^{-1}.

The conformation of the polymer chains in oriented samples of poly(ethylene terephthalate) was investigated by Dulmage and Geddes[67], Grime and Ward[92], Miyake[193,194,195], Schmidt[285], Tadokoro et al.[329], and others.

There is a rotational isomerism in the —O—CH$_2$—CH$_2$—O— portion of the chain. Bands at 1470, 1340, 975, and 850 cm^{-1} were attributed to the *trans*-conformation of the CH_2 groups in the crystalline regions, while bands at 1445, 1370, 1045, and 895 cm^{-1} are to be associated with the *gauche*-conformation of the CH_2 groups. During crystallization the configuration of the ethylene glycol residue seems to change from *gauche* to *trans* (see, however, Schmidt[286]). Interestingly, most of the bands being sensitive to crystallinity belong to vibrational modes of the ethylene glycol units in the polymer.

TABLE 21. Infrared Bands of Poly(ethylene Terephthalate) Sensitive to Crystallization According to Tadokoro *et al.*[329]

Crystalline	Amorphous	Molten	Relative intensity	Changes with crystallization
	Wavenumber (cm^{-1})			
3430	3432	3435	w	increase in intensity
3100	3100	—	vw	disappears in molten state
3011	—	—	vw	appears in crystalline form
1473	—	—	m	appears in crystalline form
1455	1455	1455	m	decrease in intensity
1378	—	—	vvw	appears in crystalline form
1371	1370	1368	w	decrease in intensity
1344	1339	1337	s	increase in intensity
1119	1117	1115 (sh)	s	increase in intensity
1102	1100	1093	s	decrease in intensity
1040	1040	1035 (sh)	w	distinguished in quenched samples, but not in the melt
970	970	962	m	increase in intensity
845	840	—	mw	increase in intensity, disappears in molten state

Symbols: w = weak; m = medium; s = strong; v = very; sh = shoulder.

The assignments were made with the assumption that the C—C_6H_4—C part of the chain can be classified in terms of the V_h symmetry of *para*-disubstituted benzene derivatives. However, a number of absorptions forbidden in the infrared but Raman active (exclusion rule) actually can be observed in the infrared spectrum. This is due to the loss of the center of symmetry by the rotation of chain members out of the plane of the benzene rings. For the assignment of the normal modes of the —O—CH_2— CH_2—O— unit, a symmetry C_{2h} for the *trans*-1,2-substituted ethane was assumed. This structure is implied by the molecular structure of crystalline poly(ethylene terephthalate) according to Daubeny *et al.*[59].

In a recent study Schmidt[286] found that the *trans*-form of the ethylene glycol linkage is the extended form, and the *gauche*-form is the relaxed form. Furthermore, both the amorphous and the crystalline regions of poly(ethylene terephthalate) have been found to contain both of these conformations. A film with given percentage of crystallinity may therefore have varying amounts of *trans*- and *gauche*-structures. Likewise, a film with a given percentage of *trans*-structure may have varying amounts of crystalline and amorphous structures.

b. *Polyester Resins Based Upon Terephthalic Acid*

The principal use of terephthalic acid polyesters other than those with ethylene glycol is for wire enamels. Usually a mixture of glycerol and ethylene glycol is used for the esterification of the acid. The resulting polyester contains a considerable number of free hydroxyl groups which crosslink at higher temperatures. The resin is poorly soluble in the usual solvents but readily soluble in a technical mixture of phenols, cresols, and xylenols.

The infrared and gas-chromatographic analysis of lacquers of this type was described by Hummel[112]. The far infrared spectrum (Figure 48) is distinctly different from that of poly(ethylene terephthalate). This is mainly due to the high crystallinity of the latter. Surface coating resins based on terephthalic acid are amorphous.

5. STYRENATED ALKYD RESINS AND VEGETABLE OILS

Oil-modified alkyd resins can be further modified with styrene. The reaction takes place at the double bonds of the unsaturated fatty acids of the oil-component, and polystyrene chains of different length are formed. Surface coatings with these types of resins show higher resistance against aging and chemicals.

The far infrared spectrum of a styrenated alkyd resin (Figure 49) shows the strong band of polystyrene around 540 cm^{-1} superimposed by the strong and broad band of alkyds near 560 cm^{-1}.

Vinyltoluene can be used instead of styrene as a modifying agent, and unsaturated vegetable oils in place of alkyd resins. In the far infrared spectrum of a vinyltoluene modified vegetable oil (Figure 50) a band near 440 cm^{-1} is characteristic for the polymeric vinyltoluene component.

6. UNSATURATED POLYESTER RESINS

The conventional unsaturated polyester resins are usually based upon a polyester from maleic acid, phthalic acid, adipic acid, and a glycol. However, there are many variations in the type of unsaturated and saturated acids, and also in the kind of diols, to meet certain industrial specifications. These resins are dissolved in styrene or in another suitable monomer like diallyl phthalate or triallyl cyanurate. The polymerization is usually initiated by the addition of a radical catalyst.

For the identification of an uncured sample, the resin and the monomer are separated by evaporation or by suitable solvents. The far infrared spectra of styrene-free samples (Figures 51 and 52) show the characteristic band of phthalic acid esters at 650 cm^{-1}, together with bands of the other components at 670, 640, and 563 cm^{-1}. However, this picture may change considerably from one type of unsaturated polyester to another.

7. POLYCARBONATES

The most interesting polyester of carbonic acid is based on bisphenol A, and has the following monomer unit:

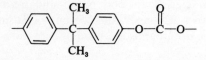

It has found considerable use as a thermoplastic material for heat-resistant and unbreakable household items and films. A structure for the molecule in the crystalline regions of the polymer has been proposed by Prietzschk[258] on the basis of preliminary x-ray diffraction studies. However, Krimm[152] stated in a recent publication that this proposed structure is in significant disagreement with x-ray and infrared data.

The far infrared spectrum of a film of polycarbonate on base of bisphenol A (Figure 53) shows only one strong band at 555 cm^{-1}, which is also present in the spectra of epoxy resins based on bisphenol A. This band must be assigned to an out-of-plane bending vibration of the *para*-substituted benzene ring; its wavenumber is in very good agreement with the value calculated by Shimanouchi *et al.*[299] (see Table 8). Bands at about 630, 485, and 350 or 390 cm^{-1} probably belong to deformation vibrations of the —O—C—O— group.

$$\overset{\|}{\underset{O}{}}$$

8. ROSIN AND ITS DERIVATIVES, OTHER NATURAL RESINS

Natural resins can be divided into three large groups according to their chemical structure: acid resins, ester resins, and hydrocarbon resins. There is, however, no clean separation between these groups. Natural resins are usually complex and not yet fully analyzed mixtures containing acids, esters, carboxylic salts, and other compounds of mainly hydrocarbon nature.

Rosin from conifers consists mainly of abietic acid and isomeric abietic acids. The structure is too complicated for a complete infrared analysis. However, the di-α-branched (quaternary) carbonyl group behaves exactly like the other carboxylic acids of this type studied by Bentley *et al.*[22]. These authors found for di-α-branched aliphatic acids one strong band between about 610 cm^{-1} and 665 cm^{-1}. There is a strong band at 657

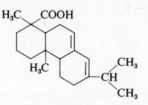

cm^{-1} in the far infrared spectrum of rosin (Figure 54). Another medium to strong band characteristic for both mono- and di-α-branched aliphatic acids appears between 520 cm^{-1} and 555 cm^{-1}. Rosin shows this band at about 538 cm^{-1}. Both bands are bending vibrations of the associated carboxylic groups.

Rosin glyceryl ester (Figure 55) has a number of bands in common with rosin itself: 704, 606, 562, and 483 cm^{-1}; it is likely that some of these bands are characteristic for the molecular skeleton of abietic acid.

Maleinate resins are obtained by a Diels–Alder addition of maleic anhydride to rosin. They are usually esterified with polyvalent alcohols. The far infrared spectrum of a maleinate resin (Figure 56) also shows the bands at 604, 560, and around 475 cm^{-1} possibly characteristic for derivatives of abietic acid.

Guaiac is a dark green to brown–black resin obtained from the trunk of *Guaiacum officinale*. It is mainly used in the pharmaceutical industry and as a reagent. The bands at about 620, 555, and 440 cm^{-1} in its far infrared spectrum (Figure 57) are characteristic for the aromatic constituents.

9. POLYVINYL ACETATE

Vinyl acetate is readily polymerizable with radical catalysts; the amorphous polymers are highly branched. They have found widespread use as binders in surface coatings and cements, for fuel-resistant pipes, and so on.

The infrared spectrum of polyvinyl acetate was studied by Melville *et al.*[187], the Raman spectrum by Simon *et al.*[307]. The strongest band in its far infrared spectrum (Figure 59) is at 605 cm^{-1}, a corresponding Raman band was found at 606 cm^{-1} (Simon *et al.*[307]). This absorption has to be assigned to a bending vibration of the acetate group. Thompson and Torkington[334] described two bands in the far infrared as being characteristic for acetates; one near 612 cm^{-1}, the other near 640 cm^{-1}. The band at 630 cm^{-1} in the spectrum of polyvinyl acetate may be this second acetate band. A fairly strong Raman line is found at 632 cm^{-1}. Most of the other far infrared bands are paralleled by corresponding Raman lines except the one at about 511 cm^{-1}. On the other hand, a very weak Raman line at 462 cm^{-1} has no corresponding line in the infrared. Both are weak and may be due to bending vibrations of the polyvinyl chain.

E. Polymers of Acrylic and Methacrylic Acids and Esters (Chart V)

1. POLYACRYLIC ACID AND POLYMETHACRYLIC ACID; SALTS OF THESE ACIDS

The far infrared spectrum of polyacrylic acid (Figure 60) shows three fairly strong bands near 630, 515, and 350 cm^{-1}. The first two bands are found in the ranges which were given by Bentley et al.[22] for mono-α-branched carboxylic acids. Wilmshurst[352] assigned absorption bands at 654 cm^{-1} and 536 cm^{-1} of gaseous acetic acid to δ_{OCO} and ρ_{CO_2} modes, respectively. The band at 350 cm^{-1} probably belongs to an out-of-plane deformation vibration of the associated carboxyl groups. Part of the Raman spectrum of polyacrylic acid was published by Simon et al.[307].

The far infrared spectrum of polymethacrylic acid (Figure 65) is markedly different from that of polyacrylic acid. The first two far infrared bands of α-branched carboxylic acids are found here at 612 cm^{-1} and 535 cm^{-1}. A new band appears near 270 cm^{-1} and may be due to a torsional vibration of the methyl group.

The infrared spectrum of the sodium salt of polyacrylic acid (Figure 61) shows four distinct absorption bands between 800 cm^{-1} and 200 cm^{-1}. According to their intensity they should belong to vibrations of the

carboxylate group. The $-C\begin{smallmatrix} \ddot{O}: \\ \\ \ddot{O}: \end{smallmatrix}$ group in its vibrational behaviour can

roughly be compared with the methylene group. A tentative assignment for the strongest long wavelength absorption bands therefore would be: CO_2-bending (782 cm^{-1}), CO_2-wagging (621 cm^{-1}), CO_2-rocking (514 cm^{-1}), and CO_2-twisting (216 cm^{-1}). The weaker absorption bands in the long wavelength region belong to bending vibrations of the polyvinyl chain.

2. POLYACRYLIC ESTERS

Esters of acrylic acids with lower aliphatic alcohols polymerize readily with radical catalysts to form polymers with lower softening points than the corresponding polymethacrylic esters. With increasing molecular weight of the alcoholic component the polymers gradually become soft resins.

3

The monomer unit

$$-CH-CH_2-$$
$$|$$
$$COOR$$

in polyacrylic esters contains a pseudo-asymmetric carbon atom. Consequently, stereospecific polymerization of acrylic esters leads to the formation of isotactic or syndiotactic polymers. Stereospecific catalysts for the polymerization of monomers containing electronegative groups are organometallic compounds like butyllithium, phenyllithium, phenylmagnesium bromide, and others. Interestingly, Garrett et al.[83] show for the acrylic esters that low temperatures $< -70°C$ favor the syndiotactic addition of monomer units to a growing chain so that radical initiation by ultraviolet or γ-radiation at low temperatures yields crystallizable polymers.

The following authors studied the infrared spectra of stereoregular polyacrylic esters: Miller and Rauhut[189, 190], crystalline p-t-butyl acrylate; Garrett et al.[83], crystalline polyalkyl acrylates with different alkyl substituents; Kawasaki et al.[137], stereoregular polymers of n-, s-, and t-butyl acrylate, Kawasaki et al.[134], stereoregular polyethyl and polypropyl thiolacrylates; Nakayama et al.[214], stereoregular polyalkyl thiolacrylates.

Part of the Raman spectrum of polyethyl acrylate was published by Simon et al.[307]. The infrared spectra of copolymers of styrene with acrylic acid derivatives were studied by Teyssie and Smets[333]. Schurz et al.[291] studied the infrared spectra of all kinds of polyacrylic acid derivatives.

The far infrared spectra of polyacrylic esters with unbranched alkyl substituents (Figures 62–64) are somewhat surprising in that they do not show an absorption of significant intensity between about 550 cm^{-1} and 650 cm^{-1} (see Lucier and Bentley[177]). The strongest band in the FIR appears between 370 cm^{-1} and 330 cm^{-1}; with increasing size of the side chain, its maximum shifts to lower wavenumbers. A second broad and intense band arises at the short wavelength flank of the main absorption. It also seems to shift to lower wavenumbers with increasing size of the side chain.

3. POLYMETHACRYLIC ESTERS

Methacrylic acid esters polymerize readily with radical catalysts to form non-crystallizable and probably mainly atactic polymers. Polymethacrylates are more rigid than the corresponding polyacrylates, and have found widespread use in industry.

A comprehensive study on the infrared spectra of methacrylic esters and their polymers was done by Salomon et al.[274]. The far infrared was covered between 700 cm^{-1} and 400 cm^{-1}. Our own results agree well with those of the authors mentioned. An infrared spectroscopic method for the determination of double bonds in poly(methyl methacrylate) was developed by Loshaek and Fox[175]. The infrared spectra of styrene–methyl methacrylate copolymers were studied by Axelrod[8]. Stroupe and Hughes[319] published a study on the structure of poly(methyl methacrylate).

By the use of stereospecific catalysts previously described for polyacrylates in this report, stereoregular and crystallizable polymers can be obtained. Fox et al.[77] described three types of poly(methyl methacrylate) with different x-ray patterns and different other properties both in the crystalline and amorphous states (see Table 22).

TABLE 22. Properties of Different Poly(Methyl Methacrylates) (According to Fox et al.[77])

Type	Glass temp., °C	Melting point, °C	Density, 30°C (Amorphous) gml^{-3}	Polymerization conditions	Presumed chain configuration
I	115	200	1.19	Free radical at low temp.; anionic in highly solvating media	Isotactic, crystallizable
II	45	160	1.22	Organolithium cpds. (anionic) in hydrocarbons	Syndiotactic, crystallizable
III	60–95	170	1.20–1.22	Anionic at low temp. in media of moderate solvating power for cations	Isotactic-syndiotactic block-copolymer
Conventional	104	—	1.188	Radical catalysts at room temp.	Essentially random within a certain degree of syndiotacticity

In another publication, Fox et al.[78] stated that for steric reasons isotactic addition of monomer units to growing chains should be favored at lower temperatures, whereas higher polymerization temperatures should favor syndiotactic growth.

The infrared spectra of stereoregular poly(methyl methacrylates) were studied by a number of authors. Fox et al.[78] found large spectral differences near 1065 cm^{-1} and 750 cm^{-1} in the spectra of differently polymerized samples, both in the crystalline and in the amorphous states. Miller et al.[191] found characteristic bands near 955 cm^{-1} and 755 cm^{-1} in the spectrum of a crystalline polymer of presumable isotactic structure;

bands present in the spectrum of a conventional polymer near 1063, 965, 913, 825, and 747 cm^{-1} were missing. Baumann et al.[11], on the other hand, found no bands characteristic for an isotactic structure in the rocksalt range. They noted, however, that bands near 1475, 1060, 965, 909, 824, and 806 cm^{-1} present in the spectra of both syndiotactic and conventional poly(methyl methacrylates) are missing in the spectrum of an isotactic polymer. Most obvious is the disappearance of a band near 1060 cm^{-1} in the spectrum of isotactic samples. From their results, Baumann et al.[11] concluded that conventional poly(methyl methacrylate) has a structure with exceeding syndiotactic arrangement. Fox et al.[78], Baumann et al.[11], and Kawasaki et al.[133] found that a number of bands, especially the one near 1060 cm^{-1}, can be found almost unchanged also in the spectra of dissolved or amorphous syndiotactic PMMA. (The "F-polymer" of Kawasaki et al.[133] is probably identical to the isotactic samples of other authors.) Korotkov et al.[145] describe bands near 962 cm^{-1} and 854 cm^{-1} as characteristic for isotactic poly(methyl methacrylate) which are missing from the spectrum of a conventional polymer.

The results of the different authors on the infrared spectrum and structure of different samples of poly(methyl methacrylate) are partially contradictory and do not yield a clear picture. However, it can be accepted as established that there exist different crystallizable polymers of methyl methacrylate which are non-polymorphous to each other and possess different stereoregular structures. As to the conventional poly(methyl methacrylate), it is rather likely that it contains a large number of syndiotactic arrangements.

The far infrared spectrum between 15 μ and 24 μ of different samples of poly(methyl methacrylate) was studied by Hummel and Busse[115] (see Figures 66 and 67). These authors found a band near 557 cm^{-1} which is much stronger in isotactic than in syndiotactic samples. The maximum of the band in syndiotactic samples is near 552 cm^{-1}. A doublet with maxima at about 506 cm^{-1} and 482 cm^{-1} is also sensitive to tacticity. The component at 506 cm^{-1} increases with the increasing amount of syndiotactic structures in the polymer.

Figure 68 shows a sample which was prepared by polymerization at 100°C with dibenzoyl peroxide. The shape of the doublet with maxima near 480 cm^{-1} and 506 cm^{-1} lies between the extremes represented by isotactic (Figure 66) and syndiotactic samples (Figure 67).

The spectra of higher polymethacrylates (Figures 69–71) show that substituents strongly influence the frequency position of the bending vibrations of the ester group. Thus, polymethacrylates can easily be identified by their far infrared spectra.

F. Cellulose Derivatives (Chart VI)

1. REGENERATED CELLULOSE AND CELLULOSE ETHERS

The far infrared spectra of cellulose (Figure 72) and its alkyl ethers (Figures 73 and 74) show a broad absorption band ranging from about 700 cm^{-1} to 300 cm^{-1}. We have to assume that the bending vibrations of the OH groups and of the glucosidic ether linkages are strongly coupled. In other words, the high absorption background is proof for strong intra- and probably intermolecular interactions. From an analytical standpoint, the far infrared spectra of cellulose ethers are of little value.

2. CELLULOSE ESTERS

The far infrared spectra of cellulose esters (Figures 75 to 79) are more significant than those of the ethers. Cellulose nitrate (Figure 79) is one exception, since organic nitrates do not have strong far infrared absorptions. The strongest band in the far infrared spectra of the carboxylic acid esters is around 600 cm^{-1}. It probably belongs to a bending vibration of the acyl groups attached to the secondary CH—O groups in the glucose units.

G. Polyethers and Ether Resins (Chart VII)

1. LINEAR ALIPHATIC POLYETHERS

Linear aliphatic polyethers with the general structure $[(CH_2)_mO]_n$ can be prepared by polymerization of the cyclic oxides of the general formula $(CH_2)_nO$. The polymerization usually has an anionic or cationic mechanism and can be initiated, for example, by bases or Lewis acids.

Linear aliphatic polyethers usually have a helical structure. Miyazawa[196] described a general method of normal coordinate treatment by internal coordinates for the vibrational spectra of chain molecules of the general structures $(CH_2)_n$, $(CH_2O)_n$, and $(CH_2OCH_2)_n$. Tadokoro[321] derived a method for the numerical calculation of the normal vibrations of helical molecules and used it for the evaluation of the infrared spectrum of polyoxymethylene.

a. Polyoxymethylene

The first member of the series of cyclic aliphatic oxides is formaldehyde ($n = 1$). It polymerizes readily on standing and forms a crystalline and brittle polymer called "paraformaldehyde," which is a mixture of polymers containing between 8 and 100 monomer units. It took twelve years and fifty million dollars to develop a polyoxymethylene which has a very high molecular weight and is known as "Delrin" (Figure 80) and manufactured by Du Pont. Meanwhile, polyoxymethylene is also produced by other companies ("Celcon" of Celanese, "Hostaform" of Farbwerke Hoechst).

The technical polyoxymethylene is highly crystalline, has blocked end-groups to prevent zip-depolymerization, and is soluble only in a few solvents like hot dimethyl sulfoxide or dimethylformamide. It has a helical structure with nine monomer units and five turns in the identity period of 17.3 Å. For better heat resistance and improved manufacturing qualities formaldehyde is sometimes copolymerized with a small amount of ethylene oxide ("Hostaform" of Farbwerke Hoechst).

The infrared spectrum of polyoxymethylene, and the spectra of lower polyformaldehydes, were studied by a number of authors (Novak and Whalley[237,238], and Tadokoro and his collaborators[323,324,325]).

Complete assignments of the infrared bands of polyoxymethylene and polyoxymethylene-d_2 are given in the recent paper of Tadokoro et al.[323]. Since the monomer unit of polyoxymethylene is very simple there is a good agreement between the calculated and the observed frequencies in the infrared spectrum of the polymer.

The far infrared spectrum of polyoxymethylene was studied in detail by Tadokoro et al.[324,325]. The results of these authors, together with our own, are shown in Table 23.

TABLE 23. Far Infrared Absorptions of Helical, Crystalline Polyoxymethylene

Tadokoro et al.[324,325]	This report	Dichroic behavior	Intensity	Assignment
Wavenumber (cm^{-1})				
630–633	629	⊥	s	δ(O—C—O) (E$_1$) (90%), mixed with γ_a(C—O—C)
455–458	450	⊥	m	δ(C—O—C) (E$_1$) (76%), mixed with γ_r(CH$_2$)
235	Not determined	‖	w	Torsional Vibration of the C—O—C chain, A$_2$
22 (calculated)	Not determined	Not determined	—	Torsional vibration of the C—O—C chain, A$_1$

Symbols: w = weak; m = medium; s = strong.

b. *Polyoxyethylene*

Ethylene oxide,

$$CH_2\text{—}CH_2,$$
$$\diagdown\diagup$$
$$O$$

can be polymerized to form liquid or wax-like polymers. In the absence of water and other chain-terminating reagents with active hydrogen atoms, fibrous high-polymers with molecular weights around 10^6 can be obtained. In contrast to polyoxymethylene, these polymers are readily soluble in water up to the highest molecular weights obtained. Apparently the intermolecular interactions between the polyoxyethylene chains are lower, and allow the water molecules to separate the chains by forming hydrogen bridges.

Crystalline polyoxyethylene also has helical chains with a fiber period of 19.25 Å. Davison[61], from his infrared data, assumed a threefold helix and a *gauche*-conformation of the monomer units. Miyake[193] later altered Davison's assignment and assumed monomer units in both the *trans*- and *gauche*-conformations. Miyazawa et al.[199] did not agree with the earlier assignments and conclusions and made another careful examination of the infrared spectrum between 3500 cm^{-1} and 50 cm^{-1} of highly oriented crystalline films. Measurements with polarized infrared were made between 3500 cm^{-1} and 400 cm^{-1}. According to these authors, the most likely model with *trans–gauche–trans*-conformation contains seven monomer units and two helical turns per fiber period of 19.25 Å.

TABLE 24. Far Infrared Bands of Polyoxyethylene

Miyazawa et al.[199]	This report	Dichroic behavior	Potential energy distribution (%)
Wavenumber (cm^{-1})			
	640	Not determined	
	577⎫	Not determined	
	560⎭	Not determined	
529	527⎫	∥	
508	507⎭	∥	δ(CCO) (A$_2$) (100)
(485)*	455 (sh)	Not determined	
(372)*	380	Not determined	
	355	Not determined	
	324	Not determined	
216		⊥	δ(CCO) (35), γ_t(CC) (35), δ(COC) (25); E(θ)
165		⊥	γ_t(CO) (35) γ_t(CC) (30), δ(CCO) (25); E(θ)
107		∥	γ_t(CO) (85)

* Calculated but not observed by Miyazawa et al.[199]

Low molecular weight polyoxyethylene glycols are liquids. The infrared spectra were studied by Davison[61], and Kuroda and Kubo[158,159]. The far infrared spectrum of a liquid polyoxyethylene glycol (Figure 81) shows only one fairly strong absorption band due to a C—O—C bending vibration with a maximum ranging between 560 cm^{-1} and 520 cm^{-1}. A second broad band near 260 cm^{-1} is probably due to a torsional vibration of the chain.

The far infrared spectrum of a highly crystalline polyoxyethylene with a molecular weight about 8.10^5 (Figure 82) differs strongly from that of a liquid polyoxyethylene glycol. The C—O—C bending vibration has split into two components at 527 cm^{-1} and 507 cm^{-1}, and a number of new, weak bands has appeared at the low frequency end of the spectrum. The results of Miyazawa et al.[199] together with ours are shown in Table 24.

c. *Polyoxypropylene*

Propylene oxide,

$$CH_2—\overset{*}{C}H—CH_3$$
$$\diagdown O \diagup$$

has an asymmetric carbon atom in its molecule, and consequently can occur in a *d*-form and in an *l*-form. Price et al.[257] described the formation of a crystallizable and optically active polyoxypropylene by the polymerization of *l*-propylene oxide. They explained the optical activity with an all-*l* structure of the polymer. Other polymerization conditions yielded a crystallizable but optically inactive polymer apparently consisting of a racemic mixture of all-*d* and all-*l* forms. The infrared spectrum of crystalline polyoxypropylene was described by Price and Osgan[256] and Kawasaki et al.[135].

With normal ionic catalysts and with the racemic mixture of propylene oxide, liquid or paste-like polymers with relatively low molecular weights are formed. Only the lower members of the homologous series show a slight solubility in water.

The far infrared spectrum of a liquid polyoxypropylene (Figure 83) is rather indistinct. A very broad band between 600 cm^{-1} and 400 cm^{-1} is due to bending vibrations of the C—O—C groups, and out-of-plane deformation vibrations of hydroxyl end-groups.

2. OTHER, ILL-DEFINED POLYETHERS

Another group of resinous aliphatic ethers are the self-condensation products of aldehydes and ketones. Acetaldehyde aldolizes to yield

$$H_3C—CH—CH_2—CHO$$
$$\qquad |$$
$$\qquad OH$$

This in turn undergoes further aldolization and condensation, a process which finally yields a resin-like material containing alcoholic and ether groups, and also some unreacted aldehyde groups.

An infrared study on polyacetaldehyde was published by Delzenne and Smets[62]. The far infrared spectrum of an obsolete industrial acetaldehyde resin (Figure 84) is very poor. The very broad absorption between 700 cm^{-1} and 440 cm^{-1} is caused mainly by C—O—C and C—OH deformation vibrations. The assignment of the weak but sharp band at about 365 cm^{-1} is unknown.

A technical condensation product of acetophenone with formaldehyde is used as an unsaponifiable resin in surface coatings. According to its infrared spectrum, it did not contain hydroxyl groups. On the other hand, many of the C$_6$H$_5$—C— residues apparently remained unchanged. This
$$\underset{O}{\overset{\|}{}}$$
leads to the assumption that the condensation process mainly includes the activated methyl groups:

$$C_6H_5—CO—CH_3 + CH_2O \rightarrow C_6H_5—CO—CH_2—O—CH_3.$$

This keto ether may further react with its activated methylene group. The far infrared spectrum (Figure 85) contains a number of weak and medium absorption bands, some of which may be assigned to ring vibrations. There is no strong bending vibration of ether groups evident.

3. POLYVINYL ETHERS

Vinyl ethers polymerize in the presence of Lewis acids to form amorphous polymers of a soft-resin, or rubber-like nature (see Schildknecht et al.[281]). Since there is one pseudo-asymmetric carbon atom in the monomer unit,

$$—\underset{OR}{\overset{}{CH}}—CH_2—$$

stereoregular polymers with isotactic or syndiotactic structure must be possible. Schildknecht et al.[280] polymerized vinyl isobutyl ether, in analogy to former German patent of Mueller-Cunradi and Pieroh, with BF$_3$–dialkyl ether complexes ("modified Friedel–Crafts catalyst") and obtained rather rigid polymers. These could be fractionated and yielded crystallizable fractions. Later, Natta and his coworkers[220, 224] were able to obtain a number of isotactic, crystallizable polyvinyl ethers using modified Friedel–Crafts catalysts.

The infrared spectra of some polyvinyl ethers were published by Schildknecht[279]. The far infrared spectrum of an amorphous polyvinyl methyl ether (Figure 86) shows two strong bands at about 550 cm^{-1} and 410 cm^{-1}, rising above a rather high absorption background. These are probably bending vibrations involving the ether group.

The far infrared spectrum of an amorphous polyvinyl isobutyl ether (Figure 87) is more complicated. A number of bands are fused together in a broad absorption covering the range between 600 cm^{-1} and 350 cm^{-1}. Apparently the bending vibrations of the molecular skeleton couple strongly. The substitution of the methyl by an isobutyl group has put all the skeleton vibrations out of tune. This is consistent with the observation of Katon[131] that the far infrared absorptions of ethers cannot be considered as characteristic group frequencies.

4. POLYVINYL ACETALS

Polyvinyl acetals can be obtained by the reaction of polyvinyl alcohol with aldehydes. Up to about 60% of the alcoholic groups thus are included in cyclic 1,3-dioxane structures:

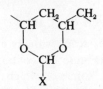

The "X" means hydrogen in the case of polyvinyl formal. The far infrared spectrum (Figure 88) of this polymer contains a sequence of medium to strong bands which may be assigned to in-plane and out-of-plane C—O—C bending vibrations of the dioxane ring systems. The spectrum of the butyral ($X = C_4H_9$) (Figure 89) is less significant. The different bands are fused together in one very broad and intense band which covers the range between about 700 cm^{-1} and 350 cm^{-1}. This is one more example of the strong coupling of vibrations in the far infrared.

5. EPOXIDES

Olefinic double bonds of the type —CH=CH— can readily be oxidized to form epoxy groups,

$$-CH-CH-$$
$$\diagdown O \diagup$$

The infrared absorption bands characteristic of the oxirane ring were studied by Shreve et al.[303] and Patterson.[245] Feazel and Verchot[73] described a simple infrared technique to study the curing of epoxy resins. A similar method was later described by Lee and Brelant[162]. Isaac[119] investigated the far infrared spectra of epoxy compounds and reported a band at about 370 cm^{-1} as being characteristic for the oxirane ring.

Figure 90 shows an aliphatic epoxy resin which contains alcoholic and ether groups in addition to the epoxy groups. The former gives rise to a very broad absorption band over the far infrared range. A superimposed band at about 365 cm^{-1} possibly arises from the epoxy groups in the resin. In the spectrum of a highly epoxidized soybean oil (Figure 91), the strongest band at about 460 cm^{-1} may be due to the epoxy groups.

Widely used in surface coating resins and in castings are aromatic epoxy resins based on bisphenol-A. The structure is:

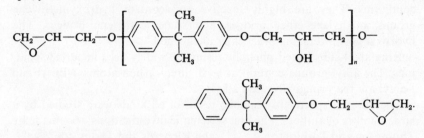

Since the epoxy groups are only at the ends of the molecule, their relative concentration decreases with increasing molecular weight of the resin. The far infrared spectra of these compounds are very characteristic (Figures 92 and 93). Both an in-plane ring bending vibration and a C—O—C bending vibration contribute to the very strong absorption at about 575 cm^{-1} to 555 cm^{-1}. The medium band at 375 cm^{-1} in the spectrum of a low-molecular liquid of this type (Figure 92) belongs to the epoxy groups and can be used for quantitative measurements.

6. COUMARONE RESINS

The olefinic double bond in coumarone,

is reactive. Polymerization is performed with acids like sulfuric acid, and leads to the formation of resinous polymers. Industrial coumarone resins usually contain only small amounts of coumarone units and up to 90% indene units. The designation "coumarone" resins is therefore misleading.

The infrared spectra of industrial coumarone–indene resins were studied by Eckardt and Heinze[68]. The far infrared spectrum of a rather complex mixture of this type (Figure 94) has its strongest band near 425 cm^{-1}. Polyindene also has its strongest far infrared band at this frequency.

H. Phenolic Resins

The hydroxyl group on the phenyl ring activates the hydrogen atoms in the *ortho*- and *para*-position to the OH group. These react with formaldehyde under acid or alkaline conditions to form "novolacs" or "resoles." The former contain roughly equimolecular amounts of phenol and aldehyde, and the links between the aromatic rings are methylene bridges. Resoles are formed with an excess of aldehyde and mainly under alkaline conditions. They are highly reactive and contain hydroxymethylene groups, methylene–ether bridges, and some methylene bridges. The hydroxyl group remains practically unchanged.

Ring alkyl-substituted phenolic resins are widely used in surface coatings. The alkyl groups contain at least three carbon atoms. *t*-Butyl and *t*-octyl are the principally used alkyls.

The infrared spectra of phenolic resins of all kinds were studied by a large number of authors. The first systematic investigations were made by Thompson and Torkington[334–337], and Richards and Thompson[267, 268]. These authors primarily studied the relation between the different types of aromatic substitutions and the frequency of the out-of-plane vibrations of the aromatic hydrogen atoms. Bender[21] studied the reactivity of differently catalyzed phenol novolacs, and their characteristic infrared absorption bands. Grisenthwaite and Hunter[94] investigated the infrared spectra of a large number of phenolic compounds, and gave rather thorough assignments for the different characteristic absorption bands of the different structures in phenolic resins. In addition to the vibrations of the aromatic hydrogen atoms they investigated the vibrations of the methylene bridges and of the hydroxymethyl group. The cause of discoloration and the role of quinone methides in curing and discoloration reactions of phenolic resins was studied by Nakamura[213]. He found that C-type phenolic resins do not show an absorption at $5.92\ \mu$ ($1690\ cm^{-1}$) which is characterizing the quinone methides. Therefore the possibility that quinone methides exist in the C-type resins is minor. Kämmerer and Dahm[128] prepared and described defined phenol–formaldehyde condensates; in their publication they show a number of infrared spectra of cyclic derivatives with methylene bridges and dimethylene–ether bridges. Cazes[46] rescanned the infrared spectra of a number of phenolic resins and showed that the absorptions between $6\ \mu$ and $7\ \mu$ can be used for the identification of the type of substitution. He studied also the in-plane deformation vibrations of the aromatic hydrogen atoms, and the characteristic vibrations of the alkyl substituents and of the phenolic hydroxyl group. Conley and Bieron[53] made a thorough study of the oxidative degradation of phenol–formaldehyde polycondensates and described a number of absorptions characteristic for different oxidation products. An empirical relation between the absorption at $12.1\ \mu$ ($826\ cm^{-1}$) and at $13.25\ \mu$ ($755\ cm^{-1}$) and the degree of cure of phenolic resins in prepregs was used by Reed and Favero[264] as an index of phenolic resin cure. Soda[312] studied the structure of *p-t*-butyl phenolic resins and α-naphthol resins by their far infrared spectra. His results in the far infrared are shown in Table 25. Since the solid resin is amorphous, it is not surprising that there is almost no difference in the spectra of the solid and the dissolved material.

TABLE 25. Far Infrared Absorptions of a *p-t*-Butyl phenol Resin, According to Soda[312]

Solid	Solution	Assignment
Wavenumber (cm^{-1})		
685	685	Substituent-characteristic band
654	653	Substituent-characteristic band
600	600	
550	548	δ(OH) out-of-plane
521	522	δ(OH) out-of-plane
474	475	

The far infrared spectra of different phenolic resins (Figures 95 to 100) were rather unpronounced and not of much use in the qualitative analysis. A high absorption background ranges from 700 cm^{-1} to about 300 cm^{-1}. As in the case of amorphous polyethers the bending vibrations of the different polar groups couple strongly, and only a few distinct bands rise above this absorption background.

To obtain more information in these cases, it is helpful to compensate the background with a grid or another device to make the bands more prominent. The spectrum of a cresole novolac (Figure 95) was thus obtained.

I. Nitrogen Containing Resins and Polymers (Chart VIII)

1. POLYAMIDES

Polyamides are widely used as thermoplastics. They contain sequences of secondary amide groups and aliphatic groups. There are two main species of polyamides. The one has the general formula

$$-R-CO-NH-R-CO-NH-,$$

and is produced by the polymerization of cyclic amides (lactams). The other one has the general formula

$$-R-CO-NH-R'-NH-CO-,$$

and is formed by polycondensation of bifunctional acids and amines.

If the aliphatic chains are simple methylene chains, the number of carbon atoms in a repeating unit is denoted by a number added to the group-name "polyamide." Thus, "polyamide-6" is a polyamide of the type I with a sequence of five methylene groups and the amide group in the repeating unit, whereas "polyamide-6,6" is a polyamide of the type II formed from adipic acid and hexamethylene diamine.

Polyamides with a regular structure are crystalline. They can, however, differ in the degree of regularity of their chain conformation and can crystallize in different polymorphous modifications. One modification is characterized by planar sheets formed by coplanar chains connected by hydrogen bridges. These sheets can be arranged in two ways; the resulting forms are usually called the α- and β-forms of polyamides. Another modification has nonplanar "pleated" sheets where the plane of the amide group and the plane of the methylene sequence in a monomer unit are twisted by a certain angle. This is usually called the γ-form. Polyamides usually crystallize in the planar α- or β-forms. The γ-form can be prepared by treatment of a polyamide film with a KI_3 solution (breaking of the hydrogen bridges), and subsequent removal of the iodine by a thiosulfate solution (rearrangement of the chains in the γ-form). The possibility of crystallization in the different polymorphous modifications depends on the chemical structure of the polyamide.

Copolyamides having different monomer units in a chain show a considerably lower degree of crystallization and also a lower melting range. On the other hand, they are more readily soluble in the conventional solvents and can be used as components in surface coatings.

The infrared spectra of polyamides were studied by numerous authors. Only the more recent and important ones are reported here. Fundamental investigations on the correlation between the infrared spectrum and the structure of polyamides were published by Cannon[44], Miyake[195], Tobin and Carrano[342], Schnell[289], and Hendus et al.[104]. The correlation between crystallinity and polymorphous modifications and the infrared spectrum of polyamides was studied by Sandeman and Keller[277], Tobin and Carrano[342], Ziabicki[359], Hendus et al.[104], and Starkweather and Moynihan[315]. King and Wood[141] determined the infrared extinction coefficients for amorphous and crystalline polyamide-6. Doskočilová et al.[66] described a method for the determination of crystallinity of copolymers of caprolactam with γ-methylcaprolactam. Shigorin et al.[298] investigated the influence of the different hydrogen bridges on the frequency of the N—H stretching vibrations of polyamide fibers. The infrared spectra of less common polyamides were studied by Doskočilová[65], poly-γ-methylcaprolactam), Schmidt and Schneider[284] (deuterated polycaprolactam) and Kinoshita[142] (a series of different polyamides).

A systematic study of the characteristic infrared bands of monosubstituted amides was published by Miyazawa, Shimanouchi, and Mizushima[204]. Chirgadse[49] finally gave the complete calculation of the vibrations of the peptide group. The author[50] also investigated the frequencies of the amide bands I and II for different conformations.

The planar and strongly polar secondary amide group with its infrared active vibrations governs the spectrum of polyamides. The characteristic bands of the secondary amide group were numbered from I to VI. Actually, all of them are sensitive to the physical state of the sample. This is due to (1) the strong hydrogen bridges within and between the chains in solid or molten samples, and (2) the strong mechanical coupling between different vibrational modes, for instance, between $\nu(C—N)$ and $\delta(NH)$.

A very valuable fact is the sensitivity of the infrared spectrum of polyamides against polymorphism. The amide bands of planar α- and β-forms, compared with the corresponding bands of the nonplanar γ-form, are generally shifted towards longer wavelengths. This is shown in Table 26. The effect of polymorphism is most pronounced in the long wavelength region. Thus, polyamides in the α- or β-forms can be easily identified by the bands near 690 cm^{-1} and 580 cm^{-1}. The same polyamides in the γ-form, absorb near 710 cm^{-1} and 625 cm^{-1}.

Table 26 shows the different characteristic bands of the secondary amide group in crystalline polyamides, together with their assignments. The values were partially taken from the literature, partially from our own

TABLE 26. Characteristic Infrared Bands of the Secondary Amide Group in Polyamides

No.	Approximate Wavenumber (cm^{-1})	Assignment	Remarks
I	1640	$\nu(C=O)$	rather insensitive against polymorphism
II	1540	$\nu(C—N) + \delta(NH)$	planar α- and β-forms
	1560		nonplanar γ-form
III	1230–1190	complex vibration of the amide group and the methylene chain	planar α- and β-forms nonplanar γ-form
IV	630–650	$\delta(C=O)$	observable only in the spectra of the iodine complexes of polyamides
V	690	$\gamma(NH)$	planar α- and β-forms
	710		nonplanar γ-form
VI	580	$\gamma(C=O)$	planar α- and β-forms
	625		nonplanar γ-form
VII	290–360	torsional vibration of the	planar α- and β-forms
	410?	$\begin{matrix} O \\ \parallel \\ C \\ \diagup \, \diagdown \\ N \quad C \end{matrix}$ group*	nonplanar γ-form

* Tentative assignment.

spectra. A seventh amide band was added which probably has to be assigned to a torsional vibration of the O=C—N group. Actually, the frequency range for this band is rather broad for one deserving the designation "characteristic frequency." However, it is a fairly strong band which can usually be identified without difficulty.

A characteristic feature of this band is that its frequency is strongly dependant both on the structure and the crystalline modification of a polyamide. In the spectra of the planar forms of polyamides the band appears in the range between 290 cm^{-1} and 360 cm^{-1}. In the spectra of the γ-forms a sharp band near 410 cm^{-1} may belong to the same vibrational mode. This, however, has not yet been confirmed. Apparently, Rilsan (polyamide 11) from formic acid solution is crystallizing mainly in the γ-form; it shows absorptions near 625 cm^{-1} and 410 cm^{-1} (Figure 104).

The far infrared spectra of polyamides (Figures 101–108), are generally very characteristic and useful for qualitative and structural analysis.

Figure 102 (polyamide-6, polycaprolactam) was obtained from seven layers of a thin film which was previously oriented in two dimensions. Apparently, the degree of crystallinity is lower than in the sample obtained from formic acid solution (Figure 101). This is indicated by the higher background and the less prominent bands. Also, the intensity of the doublet at about 725 cm^{-1} and 690 cm^{-1} has reversed. This may be explained by the presence of a certain amount of the γ-form.

Copolyamides also show a lower degree of crystallinity. Hence, in the spectrum of a terpolyamide (formed from equal parts of hexamethylene diammonium adipate, caprolactam, and the adipate of p,p'-diaminodicyclohexylmethane) the absorption background is high, and the absorption bands are broad (Figure 108).

Polyamides of a special kind are the liquid or resin-like "Versamids." They are formed by condensation of dimer and trimer unsaturated fatty acids with aliphatic polyamines. They contain free amine groups and are used as curing agents for epoxy resins. In the spectrum of one of these resins (Figure 109) the bands at about 590, 520, and 430 cm^{-1} originate from vibrations of the amide group.

2. AMINO- AND AMIDOFORMALDEHYDE RESINS

Formaldehyde reacts with active hydrogen atoms of amino or amido groups to form methylol compounds which in turn are also highly reactive. For surface coating resins, these methylol compounds are partly etherified with butanol or other aliphatic alcohols; the rest serve for the crosslinking during the curing of the film. A thorough study of the reaction of urea with formaldehyde and similar reactions (α-ureidoalkylation) was recently published by Petersen[247].

The infrared spectra of urea–formaldehyde resins were studied by Becher[18], and Becher and Griffel[19]. They found that the primary methylol ureas in acid solution, pH < 3, react in the way of a condensation reaction and mainly form methylene ureas,

$$[H(NH—CO—NH—CH_2)_nNH—CO—NH_2]$$

plus some methylol methylene ureas,

$$[HOCH_2(NH—CO—NH—CH_2)_nCH_2OH].$$

Excessive formaldehyde favors the formation of methylol groups. Acid-cured urea–formaldehyde resins contain only methylene bridges.

The far infrared spectrum of a butylated urea–formaldehyde resin (Figure 110) shows only one strong and broad band with its maximum around 655 cm^{-1}. A weak shoulder appears around 540 cm^{-1}. Both absorptions are very likely caused by bending vibrations of the $O=C\begin{smallmatrix}N\\\\N\end{smallmatrix}$ group, and of bending vibrations of the ether groups.

Melamine,

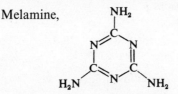

has six active hydrogen atoms which readily react with formaldehyde to form methylol groups. These in turn can be etherified, or react with amino hydrogen or other methylol groups. Melamine resins have obtained considerable application for mouldings and in surface coating lacquers.

The infrared spectra of triazine derivatives were studied by a few authors. The infrared spectra of melamine and melamine-d_6 were investigated by Jones and Orville-Thomas[125] between 5000 cm^{-1} and 450 cm^{-1}. The results indicate that the molecule is planar. Padgett and Hammer[243] studied the infrared spectra of 35 derivatives of 1,3,5-triazine. According to these authors strong bands near 6.4 μ and 6.9 μ (1560 and 1450 cm^{-1}) belong to in-plane deformation vibrations of the triazine ring system. A weaker band near 12.25 μ (815 cm^{-1}) is assigned to an out-of-plane ring vibration. The latter shifts to lower frequencies when strongly electrophilic residues like Cl or positively charged nitrogen are attached to the ring. Similar investigations were performed by Reimschuessel and McDevitt[265]. The infrared spectra of some new derivatives of s-triazine between 3333 and 670 cm^{-1}, especially ethers, amino derivatives, and sulphur containing compounds, have been investigated by Loughran *et al.*[176]. An interpretation of the spectra is given and some new assignments are made.

The far infrared spectrum of an etherified melamine–formaldehyde resin (Figure 111) similar to that of a urea–formaldehyde resin, shows only one broad and intense band with its maximum around 630 cm^{-1}. This absorption probably belongs to a C—O—C bending vibration of the ether groups. An oil-modified melamine resin showed an additional absorption from the vegetable oil at about 450 cm^{-1} (Figure 112).

Benzoguanamine resins are often used in combinations with other amino- or amidoformaldehyde resins and alkyd resins. The far infrared spectrum (Figure 113) is characterized by a strong, asymmetric band with its maximum at 645 cm^{-1} and two weaker, but rather sharp bands at 460 cm^{-1} and 320 cm^{-1}.

Sulfonamide–formaldehyde resins are less common than the other resins described above. Best known are the toluenesulfonamide resins. The far infrared spectrum of a resin of this type (Figure 114) is very pronounced by strong bands at 660, 590, and 545 cm^{-1}, caused by deformation vibrations of this group:

The infrared spectra of some sulfonamides between 4000 cm^{-1} and 400 cm^{-1} were studied by Baxter *et al.*[12].

3. OTHER NITROGEN CONTAINING RESINS AND POLYMERS

a. *Polyurethanes and Isocyanates*

Isocyanates react with active hydrogen atoms according to the following mechanism:

$$-N{=}C{=}O + H-X \longrightarrow -NH-\underset{\underset{O}{\|}}{C}-X$$

With alcohols, urethanes are formed as follows:

$$-N{=}C{=}O + ROH \longrightarrow -NH-CO-OR$$

Polyurethanes are formed by using difunctional or polyfunctional isocyanates and polyalcohols or polymers with alcoholic end groups. The reactions of isocyanates were extensively studied by Bayer and his collaborators[13,14,15], and later found tremendous industrial application.

Most of the industrially important polyurethanes, contrary to the polyesters or polyamides, do not contain the characteristic group in regular sequences. The di- or triisocyanates are used principally as connecting links between long chain polyesters or polyethers with hydroxyl end groups. Thus the specific properties of the urethane group do not determine the properties of the polymer compound.

The infrared spectra of polyurethanes were investigated by a few authors. Brumfield[39] described a method for the infrared spectrometric analysis of urethane compounds. A similar method for the quality control of curing polyurethane propellants by infrared spectrometry was described by Burns[43]. Beachell and Ngoc Son[17] studied the stabilization of polyurethanes to thermal degradation by an infrared spectroscopic method.

Polyurethanes with —NH—CO—O— as a characteristic group should exhibit spectral similarities to amides as well as esters. This is true for the rocksalt range where the carbonyl band found in urethanes absorbs near 1724 cm^{-1} and the amide II band at 1540 cm^{-1}. In the far infrared a characteristic absorption band probably arising from an out-of-plane deformation vibration of the associated NH-group often appears between 600 cm^{-1} and 650 cm^{-1}.

"Durethan U$_0$" is an aliphatic polyurethane from hexamethylene diisocyanate and 1,4-butanediol. It is exceptional in having a regular sequence of urethane groups and being based on an aliphatic isocyanate. The strongest band in its far infrared spectrum (Figure 115) has its maximum at 640 cm^{-1}. The band is rather broad and due to this fact and its wavenumber position, it resembles the amide band V of secondary amides.

The Adiprenes L-100 and L-167 are polytetrahydrofuranes which were reacted with a mixture of the isomeric toluene diisocyanates. Thus the end groups in the adiprenes have the following structures:

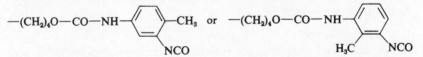

If the assignment stated above is correct, then the absorption at about 630 cm^{-1} in the spectra of the adiprenes (Figures 116 and 117) is due to the urethane groups. A similar band occurs at 620 cm^{-1} in the spectrum of "Desmodur TT stabil" (Figure 118), which is a phenylurethane of the dimerized toluene 2,4-diisocyanate. It is dubious whether the band at 613 cm^{-1} in the spectrum of "Desmodur AP stabil" (Figure 119) has the same origin. This resin is a phenylurethane of a reaction product of one mole hexanetriol and three moles toluene diisocyanate.

The infrared absorptions of the isocyanate group were studied by a few authors (Davison[60], Bailey et al.[10], and Hoyer[110]). The far infrared absorptions of this group are uncertain. There should be at least one fairly strong bending vibration of the isocyanate group as a whole:

$$\overset{\uparrow}{-C-N\overset{\downarrow}{C}O}$$

This vibration probably mixes with bending vibrations of the adjacent groups. All of the molecules containing isocyanate groups, studied by us (Figures 116–120), exhibited a fairly strong band between 550 cm^{-1} and 565 cm^{-1} and a medium but sharp band near 440 cm^{-1}. One of these may tentatively be assigned to the bending vibration shown above.

Hylene DMM has the following structure:

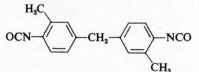

The Adiprenes have the strongest bands at 560 cm^{-1} and 445 cm^{-1}. At least the former partly stems from the ether linkages in the polytetrahydrofurane chain. Desmodur TT stabil has similar bands at 555 cm^{-1} and 445 cm^{-1}. Its structure is:

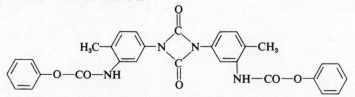

Further work is necessary to find out if this pair of bands is characteristic for the isocyanate group, whether monomeric or dimeric, or if it is related to the 1,2,4-substituted ring systems.

b. *Polyacrylonitrile*

For industrial purposes acrylonitrile is usually copolymerized with small amounts of other comonomers like vinyl acetate or acrylic acid. On the other hand, certain plastics like high-impact polystyrenes, and synthetic rubbers like the "Buna N" type butadiene copolymers contain smaller or larger amounts of acrylonitrile units in their chains.

The infrared spectrum of polyacrylonitrile was studied by a number of authors. Liang and Krimm[167] gave a rather complete assignment of the bands between 3200 cm^{-1} and 70 cm^{-1}. Table 27 shows their results for the bands below 700 cm^{-1}. Bayzer and Schurz[16] studied the ultraviolet and infrared spectra of polyacrylonitrile and its saponification products. The infrared spectrum of polyacrylonitrile prepared by γ-irradiation at room temperature was studied by Arthur and Demint[6], and Bernas[24].

They found no spectral differences between conventionally polymerized polyacrylonitrile and the radiation-polymerized polymer. Chen *et al.*[48] and Schneider[287,288] and her collaborators investigated the infrared spectrum of polyacrylonitrile prepared at $-78°C$ by irradiating the liquid monomer. They found an additional absorption band at 2030

TABLE 27. Far Infrared Absorption Bands of Polyacrylonitrile
According to Liang and Krimm[167]

Wavenumber (cm^{-1})	Intensity	Dichroic behavior	Assignment
675	w	—	Combination vibration
532	m	⊥	$\delta(C—CN)$
430	w	⊥	$\delta(CN)$
259	ms	Not determined	$\gamma_w(C—CN)$
127	vs	Not determined	$\gamma_w(CN)$
86	mw	Not determined	Subtraction vibration

Symbols: w = weak; m = medium; s = strong; vs = very strong.

cm^{-1} (4.9 μ) which is due to ketene–imine bridges which are formed by a radical mechanism during the low-temperature polymerization. Gentilhomme *et al.*[85] described the analysis of acrylonitrile copolymers by an infrared method. The detection of end-groups in acrylonitrile by differential infrared spectroscopy was described by Matsubara[183] and Yamadera[356].

The far infrared spectrum of a copolymer of acrylonitrile with about 6% vinyl acetate (Figure 121) shows, in addition to the bands of polyacrylonitrile, absorptions near 603 cm^{-1} and 630 cm^{-1} belonging to vibrations of the vinyl acetate units.

c. *Polyvinylcarbazole*

Polyvinylcarbazole has the monomer unit

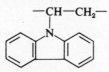

and is a very hard and high-melting resin. It has outstanding dielectric properties and is used in surface coatings.

Its far infrared spectrum (Figure 122) is characterized by a number of pronounced bands. The one at 530 cm^{-1} is probably an in-plane bending vibration of the *ortho*-substituted rings. A fairly strong band near 420 cm^{-1} is probably caused by an out-of-plane ring bending vibration involving the nitrogen atom.

J. Silicones

The name "silicone" is derived from "ketone" since both have analogous general formulas: R—CO—R' and (R—SiO—R')$_n$. However, Si is not able to form double bonds, and therefore the term "polysiloxane" is more correct.

The most commonly used silicones are the polydimethylsiloxane and the polymethylphenylsiloxane. The former is the main constituent in silicone rubbers, the latter is often found in resin combinations for high-temperature surface coatings.

The infrared spectra of polysiloxanes and similar silicon compounds were extensively studied. The first detailed study on the infrared spectra of cyclic and linear methylpolysiloxanes was published by Wright and Hunter[354]. Richards and Thompson[268] investigated the spectra of some silicones and related substances between 2 μ and 20 μ. The compounds included a series of open-chain methylpolysiloxanes, cyclic methylpolysiloxanes, some alkoxysilanes, phenylsiloxanes and others. According to these authors an absorption band near 7.9 μ (1266 cm^{-1}) occurring in all compounds with Si—CH$_3$ groups belongs to a CH$_3$-rocking vibration. The bands near 11.9 μ and 12.5 μ (840 cm^{-1} and 800 cm^{-1}) in the spectra of poly(dimethylsiloxanes) belong to Si—C stretching vibrations. A band near 13.25 μ (755 cm^{-1}) not occurring in the spectra of cyclopolysiloxanes originates in a vibration of the Si(CH$_3$)$_3$ groups. An absorption band near 14.3 μ (700 cm^{-1}) is observed in the spectra of open-chain and cyclic polysiloxanes and belongs to a vibration of the Si(CH$_3$)$_2$ groups.

Further investigations on the infrared spectra of a large number of cyclic disubstituted siloxanes was performed by Young et al.[358] Infrared spectroscopic methods for the identification of organosilicon compounds of all kinds were described by Kreshkov et al.[149], Smith and his collaborators[309], Andrianov et al.[5], and Kriegsmann[150]. The infrared spectra of organosilicon compounds in the range between 667 cm^{-1} and 263 cm^{-1} (15 μ to 38 μ) were investigated by Smith[309].

Generally, vibrations involving chemical groups with silicon are about five times as strong as those of similar groups with carbon. This is also true for the far infrared where the bending vibrations of the siloxane chain and of the substituents cause extremely strong bands.

The far infrared spectrum of poly(dimethylsiloxane) (Figure 123) is comparably simple but very characteristic. Two very strong bands near 475 cm^{-1} and 385 cm^{-1} dominate the spectrum. They are very likely caused by a Si—O—Si bending, and by an O—Si—CH$_3$ bending vibration, respectively. The band near 275 cm^{-1} may be due to a methyl twisting vibration.

Similar bands, though with reversed intensity, are found in the far infrared spectrum of a poly(methylphenylsiloxane) (Figure 124). The band near 605 cm^{-1} probably belongs to an in-plane bending vibration; the one near 440 cm^{-1} to an out-of-plane bending vibration of the mono-substituted ring. The latter apparently couples with a skeleton vibration of the siloxane chain; this would explain its intensity.

Harvey and Nebergall[99] assigned a strong band near 515 cm^{-1} in the spectra of compounds with the C_6H_5—Si—C_6H_5 group to the asymmetric stretching vibration of the group C—Si—C. For methylphenylsiloxanes, we would prefer to assign tentatively the sharp and strong band at 665 cm^{-1} to a Si—phenyl stretching vibration and a band near 540 cm^{-1} to an O—Si—phenyl bending vibration.

K. Waxes and Asphalts

Aliphatic asphalts do not significantly absorb in the far infrared (Figure 125). Montan wax is a mineral wax which contains long chain fatty acids and high molecular weight aliphatic esters. The strongest band at 540 cm^{-1} in the far infrared spectrum (Figure 126) belongs to a bending vibration of the C—CO—O grouping. Beeswax is a mixture of myricyl palmitate, long chain fatty acids and small amounts of other compounds. The far infrared spectrum of the liquid (not shown) exhibits three very broad absorptions belonging to deformation vibrations of the ester and carboxylic groups. The spectrum of the crystalline wax (Figure 127) shows numerous absorption bands. The maxima at 580, 540, 430, and 400 cm^{-1} are best suited for identification. Carnauba wax is a palm wax consisting mainly of high molecular weight hydrocarbons, higher alcohols and their esters, and small amounts of other compounds. The far infrared spectrum (Figure 128) is sufficiently characteristic for an identification. The strongest band at 515 cm^{-1} belongs to the bending vibration of the ester and carbonyl groups. Candelilla wax is obtained from certain shrubs in Mexico and Japan. Chemically, it is a mixture of high molecular weight hydrocarbons and ester and acid resins. It is fairly unsaturated. Its far infrared spectrum (Figure 129) shows some similarities to the spectrum of Montan wax (Figure 126). However, the absorptivity of the strongest band at 545 cm^{-1} is about three times lower in Candelilla wax due to its content of hydrocarbons.

Generally, both natural and synthetic waxes may readily be identified by their far infrared spectra.

L. Plasticizers

1. ALIPHATIC ESTERS OF CARBOXYLIC ACIDS

The far infrared spectra of higher aliphatic esters are rather un-characteristic in showing only the absorptions of the ester group. Consequently, aliphatic ester-type plasticizers cannot be easily identified by their far infrared spectra. The main absorptions in the spectra of di-ethylhexyladipate (Figure 130) and diethyhexylsebacate (Figure 131) were at 580, 480, and about 300 cm^{-1}.

2. PHTHALATES (CHART IX)

Esters of the *o*-phthalic acid have altogether four characteristic ab-sorptions in the far infrared. The first, with one exception, is always found at exactly 650 cm^{-1}. Since it is very sharp and usually has no surrounding bands, it can be used for quantitative determinations. Only in the case of phenolic esters of the phthalic acid, the conjugated π-electron system produces a slight shift of this absorption from 650 cm^{-1} to about 655 cm^{-1}. The second, and also rather strong band occurs in the wider range between 560 cm^{-1} and 590 cm^{-1}. The third band is usually found around 400 cm^{-1}, and is partially fused with a very broad and strong band be-tween 330 cm^{-1} and 360 cm^{-1}. The other bands in the spectra of phthalate plasticizers (Figures 132–147) serve as "finger-print bands" for the identification of the individual compounds.

The assignment of the bands at 650 cm^{-1} and between 560 cm^{-1} and 590 cm^{-1} is not clear. The in-plane bending vibration of *ortho*-disub-stituted benzene derivatives was found between 495 cm^{-1} and 555 cm^{-1} as a weak to medium band. The infrared active out-of-plane ring de-formation vibration was found between 418 cm^{-1} and 470 cm^{-1} as a medium to strong band (Jakobsen[122]). On the other hand, the asym-metric bending vibration of the ester group is sometimes found as high as 650 cm^{-1}. This strongly suggests the band at 650 cm^{-1} to be an ester bending vibration. However, this vibration is known to be very sensitive to the kind of substituent, and this band in the phthalates apparently is not. Furthermore, the other band between 560 cm^{-1} and 590 cm^{-1} varies its maximum with the kind of substituent and is well in the range of a bending vibration of the ester group.

It is a likely assumption that the two carbonyl groups being conjugated to the benzene ring alter the ranges of the ring vibrations considerably. Actually, no band in the range for the out-of-plane ring deformation vibration (470–418 cm^{-1}) could be found. We should, therefore, prefer to consider the band at 650 cm^{-1} as a vibration of the aromatic system, and the next one as an ester vibration. The band near 350 cm^{-1} is probably an out-of-plane vibration of the ester group. Further assignments were not tried.

3. PHOSPHATES (CHART X)

The infrared spectra of phosphoric acid esters and similar compounds were studied by a large number of authors. Meyrick and Thompson[188] investigated the infrared and Raman spectra of alkyl esters of phosphorous oxyacids. The infrared spectra of about sixty different phosphorous compounds were studied by Daasch and Smith[55]. The authors made empirical assignments for a number of groups. A very thorough study on the infrared spectra of phosphorous compounds was also published by Bellamy and Beecher[20]. Corbridge[54] and later Nyquist[239] reinvestigated the infrared spectra of inorganic and organic phosphorous compounds and gave a number of new assignments. Mortimer[209] studied the influence of rotational isomerism on the vibrational spectra in some simple organic phosphates.

TABLE 28. Far Infrared Absorptions of Some Liquid Phosphoric Acid Esters Between 700 and 250 cm^{-1}

Trimethyl phosphate* (cm^{-1})	Triethyl phosphate* (cm^{-1})	Tri-n-butyl phosphate† (cm^{-1})	Triphenyl phosphate† (cm^{-1})	
			687	688
			620	660
			579	578
526	545	557 + 540 (sh)	565	565 (sh)
500	525	510	518	518
			497	495–505
459	465	463	470	460 (sh)
		425		
		363		
		275		

* Mortimer[209].   † This report.   Symbol: sh = shoulder.

Owing to the strong polarity of the phosphate group, its stretching and deformation vibrations give rise to intense absorptions both in the rock-salt range and in the far infrared. Table 28 shows the far infrared absorptions of some phosphoric acid esters between 700 cm^{-1} and 250 cm^{-1}, found by Mortimer[209] and in our study. As to the assignments, it may be helpful first to consider the phosphate group as an isolated unit:

This should exhibit two infrared active bending vibrations; a symmetric one and an asymmetric one (compare the bending vibrations of a methyl group). These bending vibrations should give rise to rather strong infrared bands. If alkyl groups are attached to the three single-bonded oxygen atoms the C—O bending vibrations will appear in the spectrum, but will be coupled with the P—O bending vibrations.

Actually, the spectra of alkylphosphates show two strong bands between 525 cm^{-1} and 560 cm^{-1} and between about 400 cm^{-1} and 460 cm^{-1}. Their position in the spectrum is very sensitive to the kind of substituent. Other bands, partially fused with the ones mentioned above, occur in the same range but are somewhat weaker. They are also sensitive to the kind of substituent. This clearly shows that we have a set of mixed vibrations involving both bending of the PO$_3$ angles and bending of the C—O—P angles.

Crystallization causes considerable changes in the far infrared spectrum of phosphoric acid esters (Mortimer[209]). The ones shown in this report (Figures 148–156) were all in the liquid state.

M. Monomers (Chart XI)

Olefin-type monomers usually have one of the two following general structures:

$$X{-}CH{=}CH_2 \quad \text{or} \quad \substack{Y \\ \diagdown \\ \diagup \\ Z}C{=}CH_2$$

(vinyl type)   (vinylidene type)

Both the vinyl and the vinylidene group have very significant absorptions in the rocksalt range caused by the C=C stretching and the out-of-plane deformation vibrations of the hydrogen atoms attached to the olefinic double bond.

In the far infrared we may expect a torsional vibration of the =CH$_2$ group, and deformation vibrations of the substituents X, Y, or Z of the following types (simplified presentation):

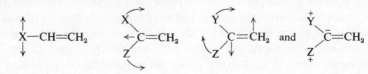

Bentley and Wolfarth found the following absorptions of different alkenes in the far infrared (see Table 29). Harrah and Mayo[97] later found that all 1-alkenes, with the exception of propene, exhibit two infrared bands of medium intensity near 630 cm^{-1} and 550 cm^{-1}. Both bands are caused by

TABLE 29. Far Infrared Absorptions of Alkenes According to Bentley and Wolfarth[23]

Unbranched (cm^{-1})	1-Alkenes α-branched (cm^{-1})	Remote branch (cm^{-1})	cis-2-Alkenes (cm^{-1})	trans-2-Alkenes (cm^{-1})
637–629		625–614	588–571	417–385
554–549	559–532		488–465	323–286

a vibration of the vinyl group, probably the torsional vibration of the $=CH_2$ group. It is very likely that the band near 550 cm^{-1} belongs to an almost planar conformation of the vinyl group with the C^2—C^4 plane. The band near 630 cm^{-1} probably belongs to the more stable conformation where the vinyl group is rotated around the C^2—C^3 bond by angles of $\pm 30°$ or $\pm 90°$. Apparently branching of the alkyl chain may favor one or the other conformation, as suggested by the results of Bentley and Wolfarth.[23]

The in-plane bending vibration of the C=C—X group (X = C or O) was found for propene (Rasmussen and Brattain[263]) near 417 cm^{-1}, for 1-butene (Sheppard[295]) near 437 cm^{-1}, and for vinyl ethers (Popov and Kagan[255]) between 421 cm^{-1} and 478 cm^{-1}, depending on the conformation of the molecule.

Most of the olefin-type monomers studied in this report exhibit a band between about 375 cm^{-1} and 430 cm^{-1} in their far infrared spectra (Figures 158–174). The intensity is varying from weak to strong depending upon the substituents. We assign this band tentatively to the C—C=C in-plane bending vibration.

Vinylidene-type monomers with the general structure:

$$\begin{array}{c} Y \\ \diagdown \\ C{=}CH_2 \\ \diagup \\ Z \end{array}$$

usually exhibit a medium band between 505 cm^{-1} and 540 cm^{-1}. It is not unlikely that this band is caused by the asymmetric in-plane bending vibration of the Y—C—Z group. However, neither the assignment nor the range given here can be considered as final, especially since this vibration, in its nature and its frequency, depends upon the nature of the substituents.

Aromatic monomers (Figures 160–162) show additional bands due to deformation vibrations of the aromatic ring system.

Ester type monomers display absorptions of the ester group around 650 cm^{-1} and 350 cm^{-1}. In addition to these, methacrylates are well characterized by a doublet at 590 cm^{-1} and 600 cm^{-1} probably arising from the α-methyl group.

N. Solvents

The spectra (Figures 175–192) show a number of substances which are frequently used as solvents for polymers and resins, or as dispersants for mulls (paraffin oil). Since small amounts of the solvent frequently cannot be removed from the polymer even by long drying in a vacuum oven, it is very important to know where the strongest bands of the solvent may occur in the spectrum. In some cases, the polymer may interact with the remaining solvent molecules in a way that small shifts in the band maximum, and also changes in the absorptivity of the bands occur.

Chloroform is a very good solvent for many polymers and resins. Unfortunately, it often sticks tenaciously in the sample and adulterates the spectrum with its strong or medium bands at 667, 625, and 365 cm^{-1} (Figure 178). Since methylene chloride is also an excellent solvent and does not absorb too much in these ranges (Figure 177), it is sometimes advisable to make use of this solvent. Evaporation of methylene chloride from the film should not be performed too rapidly because water will then condense and spoil the film.

A very reasonable solvent for the far infrared is benzene (Figure 190) since it has only one weak absorption at 395 cm^{-1} in the range between 600 cm^{-1} and 300 cm^{-1}. Rather universal solvents are dimethyl sulfoxide (Figure 188) and dimethylformamide (Figure 189). Both do not absorb between about 650 cm^{-1} and 400 cm^{-1}. Due to the similarity in structure the spectra are also rather similar.

IV

References

1. Abe, K. and Yanagisawa, K., *J. Polymer Sci.*, **36**, 536 (1959).
2. Addink, E. J. and Beintema, J., *Polymer*, **2**, 185 (1961).
3. Allirot, R. and Orsini, L., *J. Chim. Phys.*, **49**, 422 (1952).
4. Ambrose, E. J., Elliot, A. and Temple, R. B., *Proc. Roy. Soc. (London)*, *Ser. A*, **199**, 183 (1949).
5. Andrianov, K. A., Gashnikova, N. P. and Aznovich, E. Z., *Bull Acad. Sci. USSR, Div. Chem. Sci. (English Transl.)*, **1960**, 800.
6. Arthur, J. C. and Demint, R. J., *J. Phys. Chem.*, **64**, 1332 (1960).
7. Asahina, M. and Enomoto, S., *Nippon Kagaku Zasshi*, **81**, 1011, 1370 (1960).
8. Axelrod, S., *P. B. Report*, **131**, 333 (1957).
9. Bailey, F. E., Henry, J. P., Lundberg, R. D., and Whelan, J. M., *Polymer Letters*, **2**, 447 (1964).
10. Bailey, M. E., Kirss, V. and Spaunburgh, R. G., *Ind. Eng. Chem.*, **48**, 794 (1956).
11. Baumann, U., Schreiber, H. and Tessmar, K., *Makromol. Chem.*, **36**, 81 (1960).
12. Baxter, J. N., Cymerman-Craig, J. and Willis, J. B., *J. Chem. Soc.*, **1955**, 669.
13. Bayer, O., *Angew. Chem.*, **59**, 257 (1947).
14. Bayer, O., *Farbe Lack*, **64**, 235 (1958).
15. Bayer, O., Peterson, S., Müller, E., Piepenbrink, H., Schmidt, F. and Weinbrenner, E., *Angew. Chem.*, **64**, 523 (1952).
16. Bayzer, H. and Schurz, J., *Z. Physik. Chem.*, *NF* **13**, 30, 223 (1957).
17. Beachell, H. C. and Ngoc Son, C. P., *J. Polymer Sci.*, *A* **8**, 1089 (1964).
18. Becher, H. J., *Chem. Ber.*, **89**, 1593, 1951 (1956).
19. Becher, H. J. and Griffel, F., *Chem. Ber.*, **91**, 2025, 2032 (1958).
20. Bellamy, L. J. and Beecher, L. J., *J. Chem. Soc.*, **1952**, 475, 1701; ibid. **1953**, 728.
21. Bender, H. L., *Mod. Plastics*, **302**, 136, 138, 220, 222 (1953).
22. Bentley, F. F., Ryan, M. T. and Katon, J. E., *Spectrochim. Acta.*, **20**, 685 (1964).
23. Bentley, F. F. and Wolfarth, E. F., *Spectrochim. Acta.*, **14**, 165 (1959).
24. Bernas, A., Bensasson, R., Rossi, I. and Barchewitz, P., *J. Chim. Phys.*, **59**, 442 (1962).
25. Binder, J. L., *Anal. Chem.*, **26**, 1877 (1954).
26. Binder, J. L., *J. Polymer Sci.*, *A* **1**, 37–46 (1963).
27. Binder, J. L., *J. Polymer Sci.*, *A* **1**, 47–58 (1963).
28. Binder, J. L. and Ransaw, H. C., *Analyt. Chem.*, **29**, 503 (1957).
29. Bogomolov, A. M., *Opt. Spectry. (USSR) (English Transl.)*, **12**, 99 (1962).
30. Bogomolov, A. M., *Opt. Spectry. (USSR) (English Transl.)*, **13**, 90 (1962).

31. Bogomolov, A. M., *Opt. Spectry.* (*USSR*) (*English Transl.*), **13**, 183 (1962).
32. Borello, E. and Mussa, C., *J. Polymer Sci.*, **13**, 401 (1954).
33. Brader, J. J., *J. Appl. Polymer Sci.*, **3**, 370 (1960).
34. Braun, D., Betz, W. and Kern, W., *Naturwiss.*, **46**, 444 (1959).
35. Brause, W. and Heinze, H.-O., *Kautschuk Gummi*, **11** (1958), WT 260.
36. Bro, M. I. and Sperati, C. A., *J. Polymer Sci.*, **38**, 289 (1959).
37. Brown, J. K. and Sheppard, N., *Trans. Faraday Soc.*, **48**, 128 (1952); *Proc. Roy. Soc.* (*London*), *Ser. A*, **231**, 555 (1955).
38. Brown, W. H., Ansel, R. E., Lucchesi, C. A. and McGinness, J. D., "Infrared spectroscopy, its use as an analytical tool in the field of paints and coatings." *Official Digest, March*, 1961.
39. Brumfield, H. L., TID-4500 (24th Ed.), UC-4-Chemistry; SCR-322 (*Office of Technical Services; Department of Commerce, Washington 25, D.C., USA*).
40. Bryant, W. M. D. and Voter, R. C., *J. Am. Chem. Soc.*, **75**, 6113 (1953).
41. Bunn, C. W. and Howells, E. R., *Nature*, **174**, 549 (1954).
42. Burleigh, P. H., *J. Am. Chem. Soc.*, **82**, 749 (1960).
43. Burns, E. A., *Analyt. Chem.*, **35**, 1270 (1963).
44. Cannon, C. G., *Spectrochim. Acta*, **16**, 302 (1960).
45. Canterino, P. J. and Kahle, G. R., *J. Appl. Polymer Sci.*, **6**, 20 (1962).
46. Cazes, J., *Double Liaison*, **88**, 17 (1962).
47. Checkland, P. B. and Davison, W. H. T., *Trans. Faraday Soc.*, **52**, 151 (1956).
48. Chen, C. S. H., Colthup, N., Deichert, W. and Welsh, R. L., *J. Polymers Sci.*, **45**, 247 (1960).
49. Chirgadse, Tu. N., *Biofizika*, **7**, 523 (1962) (Russian).
50. Chirgadse, Tu. N., *Biofizika*, **7**, 657 (1962) (Russian).
51. Ciampelli, F., Morero, D. and Cambini, M., *Makromol. Chem.*, **61**, 750 (1963).
52. Cobbs, W. H. and Burton, R. L., *J. Polymer Sci.*, **10**, 275 (1952).
53. Conley, R. T. and Bieron, J. F., *J. Appl. Polymer Sci.*, **7**, 103, 171 (1963).
54. Corbridge, D., *J. Appl. Chem.* (*London*), **6**, 456 (1956); *Chem. Ind.* (*London*), **1957**, 197.
55. Daasch, L. W. and Smith, D. C., *Anal. Chem.*, **23**, 853 (1951).
56. Dainton, F. S. and Sutherland, G. B. B. M., *J. Polymer Sci.*, **4**, 37 (1949).
57. Daniels, W. W. and Kitson, R. E., *J. Polymer Sci.*, **33**, 161 (1958).
58. Dasgupta, S., Pande, J. and Ramakrishnan, C., *J. Polymer Sci.*, **17**, 255 (1955).
59. Daubeny, R., Bunn, C. W. and Brown, C. J., *Proc. Roy. Soc.* (*London*), *Ser. A*, **226**, 531.
60. Davison, W. H. T., *J. Chem. Soc.*, **1953**, 3712.
61. Davison, W. H. T., *J. Chem. Soc.*, **1955**, 3270.
62. Delzenne, G. and Smets, G., *Makromol. Chem.*, **18/19**, 82 (1956).
63. Devaney, R. G. and Thompson, A. L., *Appl. Spectry.*, **12**, 154 (1958).
64. Dinsmore, H. L. and Smith, D. C., *Anal. Chem.*, **20**, 11 (1948).
65. Doskočilová, D., Pivcová, H., Schneider, B. and Čefelín, P., *Collection Czech. Chem. Commun.*, **28**, 1867 (1963).
66. Doskočilová, D., Schneider, B. and Čefelín, P., *Collection Czech. Chem. Commun.*, **28**, 2556 (1963).
67. Dulmage, W. J. and Geddes, A. L., *J. Polymer Sci.*, **31**, 499 (1958).

68. Eckardt, F. and Heinze, H., *Angew. Chem.*, **71**, 460 (1959); *Z. Anal. Chem.*, **170**, 166 (1959).
69. Elliot, A., Ambrose, E. J. and Temple, R. B., *J. Chem. Phys.*, **16**, 877 (1948).
70. Enomoto, S. and Asahina, M., *Nippon Kagaku Zasshi*, **81**, 1011–3 (1960).
71. Farrow, G., McIntosh, J. and Ward, I. M., *Makromol. Chem.*, **38**, 147 (1960).
72. Farrow, G. and Ward, I. M., *Polymer*, **1**, 330 (1960).
73. Feazel, C. E. and Verchot, E. A., *J. Polymer Sci.*, **25**, 351 (1957).
74. Field, J. E., Woodford, D. and Gehman, S., *J. Polymer Sci.*, **15**, 51 (1955).
75. Folt, V. L., Shipman, J. J. and Krimm, S., *J. Polymer Sci.*, **61**, S 17 (1962).
76. Fordham, J. W. L., Burleigh, P. H. and Sturm, C. L., *J. Polymer Sci.*, **41**, 73 (1959).
77. Fox, T. G., Garrett, B., Goode, W., Gratch, S., Kincaid, J., Spell, A. and Stroupe, J., *J. Am. Chem. Soc.*, **80**, 1768 (1958).
78. Fox, T. G., Goode, W., Gratch, S., Huggett, C., Kincaid, J., Spell, A. and Stroupe, J., *J. Polymer Sci.*, **31**, 173 (1958).
79. Fraga, D. W., *J. Polymer Sci.*, **41**, 522 (1959).
80. Fuchs, W. and Louis, D., *Makromol. Chem.*, **22**, 1 (1957).
81. Fuller, C. S., *Chem. Rev.*, **26**, 143 (1940).
82. Fuller, C. S., Frosch, C. J. and Pape, N. R., *J. Am. Chem. Soc.*, **62**, 1905 (1940).
83. Garrett, B. S., Goode, W., Gratch, S., Kincaid, J., Levesque, C., Spell, A., Stroupe, J. and Watanabe, W., *J. Am. Chem. Soc.*, **81**, 1007 (1959).
84. Garrigou-Lagrange, C., Lebas, J. M. and Josien, M.-L., *Spectrochem. Acta*, **12**, 305 (1958).
85. Gentilhomme, C., Piguet, A., Rosset, J. and Eyrand, C., *Bull. Soc. Chim. France, Ser. 5*, **27**, 901 (1960).
86. Glatt, L. and Ellis, J. W., *J. Chem. Phys.*, **19**, 449 (1951).
87. Golub, M. A., *J. Am. Chem. Soc.*, **80**, 1794 (1958).
88. Golub, M. A., *J. Am. Chem. Soc.*, **81**, 54 (1959).
89. Golub, M. A., *J. Polymer Sci.*, **25**, 373 (1957).
90. Golub, M. A. and Shipman, J. J., *Spectrochim. Acta*, **16**, 1165 (1960).
91. Gramberg, G., *Kolloid-Z.*, **175**, 119 (1961).
92. Grime, D. and Ward, I. M., *Trans. Faraday Soc.*, **54**, 959 (1958).
93. Grisenthwaite, R. J. and Hunter, R. F., *Chem. Ind.* (London), **1958**, 719, 1513; ibid. **1959**, 433.
94. Grisenthwaite, R. J. and Hunter, R. F., *J. Appl. Chem.*, **6**, 324 (1956); *Chem. Ind.* (London), **1957**,
95. Hampton, R. R., *Anal. Chem.*, **21**, 923 (1949).
96. Harlen, F., Simpson, W., Waddington, F. B., Waldron, J. D. and Baskett, A. C., *J. Polymer Sci.*, **18**, 589 (1955).
97. Harrah, L. A. and Mayo, D. W., *J. Chem. Phys.*, **33**, 298 (1960).
98. Harvey, M. C., and Ketley, A. D., *J. Appl. Polymer Sci.*, **5**, 247 (1961).
99. Harvey, M. C. and Nebergall, W. H., *Appl. Spectr.*, **16**, 12 (1962).
99a.Haslam, J. and H. A. Willis, *Identification and Analysis of Plastics*, Iliffe Books Ltd., London, 1965.
100. Hausdorff, H. H., "Analysis of polymers by infrared spectroscopy." *Presented at the Pittsburgh Conference on Analytical and Applied Spectroscopy, March 1951, Pittsburgh, Pa.*

101. Heffelfinger, C. J. and Burton, R. L., *J. Polymer Sci.*, **47**, 289 (1960).
102. Heidemann, G. and Zahn, H., *Makromol. Chem.*, **62**, 123 (1963).
103. Heinen, W., *J. Polymer Sci.*, **38**, 545 (1959).
104. Hendus, H., Schmieder, K., Schnell, O. and Wolf, K., *Festschr. Carl Wurster*, 60, 1960, p. 293, ed. by Badische Anilin and Sodafabrik, Ludwigshafen.
105. Higgins, G. M. C., *J. Polymer Sci.*, **A 2**, 1713 (1964).
106. Higgs, P. W., *Proc. Roy. Soc. (London), Ser A*, **220**, 472 (1953).
107. Hodgkins, J. E., *J. Org. Chem.*, **23**, 1369 (1958).
108. Hoffman, J. D. and Weeks, J. J., *J. Polymer Sci.*, **28**, 472 (1958).
109. Horne, S. E. *et al.*, *Ind. Eng. Chem.*, **48**, 784 (1956).
110. Hoyer, H., *Chem. Ber.*, **89**, 2677 (1956).
111. Hummel, D., *Analysis of Plastics, Lacquers, and Rubber*, Vols. I and II, Carl Hanser Verlag, Munich (1958).
112. Hummel, D., *Farbe Lack*, **65**, 440 (1959).
113. Hummel, D., *Kunststoffe*, **55**, 102 (1965).
114. Hummel, D., *Melliand Textilchem.*, **1**, 108 (1965).
115. Hummel, D. and Busse, A., "Far infrared spectra of polymers and resins and their analytical use." *International Symposium on Far Infrared Spectroscopy, Cincinnati, Ohio (August, 1962)*.
116. Hummel, D. and Lünebach, E., *Spectrochim. Acta*, **18**, 823 (1962).
117. Iimura, K. and Takeda, M., *J. Polymer Sci.*, **51**, S 51 (1961).
118. Immergut, E. H., Kollmann, G. and Malatesta, A., *J. Polymer Sci.*, **51**, S 57 (1961).
119. Isaac, R., "Applications of far infrared spectroscopy to the analysis of polymers." *International Symposium on Far Infrared Spectroscopy, Cincinnati, Ohio, August*, 1962.
120. Iwasaki, M., Aoki, M. and Kojima, R., *J. Polymer Sci.*, **25**, 377 (1957).
121. Iwasaki, M., Aoki, M. and Okuhara, K., *J. Polymer Sci.*, **26**, 116 (1957).
122. Jakobsen, R. J., "Frequency assignments of benzene derivatives in the cesium bromide region," *Technical Documentary Report No. ASD-TDR-62-895, Wright-Patterson Air Force Base, Ohio.*
123. Jakobsen, R. J. and Brewer, E. J., *Appl. Spectroscopy*, **16**, 32 (1962).
124. Johnson, J. E., *J. Appl. Polymer Sci.*, **2**, 205 (1959).
125. Jones, W. J. and Orville-Thomas, W. J., *Trans. Faraday Soc.*, **55**, 203 (1959).
126. Kagarise, R. E. and Weinberger, L. A., "Infrared spectra of plastics and resins," *U.S. Dept. of Commerce, OTS Bull. No. PB* 111438 (1954).
127. Kalb, G. H., Coffman, D. D., Ford, T. A. and Johnston, F. L., *J. Appl. Polymer Sci.*, **4**, 55 (1960).
128. Kämmerer, H. and Dahm, M., *Kunststoffe-Plastics*, **6**, 20 (1959).
129. Kämmerer, H., Rocaboy, F., Steinfort, G. and Kern, W., *Makromol. Chem.*, **53**, 80 (1962).
130. Kastorskii, A. P. and Medinkova, I. N., *Rubber Elastomers (Moscow)*, **3**, 55 (1963).
131. Katon, J. E., "The infrared spectra of selected ketones, ethers and alcohols between 15 and 35 microns," *Technical Documentary Report No. ASD-TDR-62-743, Wright-Patterson Air Force Base, Ohio.*
132. Katon, J. E. and Bentley, F. F., *Spectrochim. Acta*, **19**, 639 (1963).
133. Kawasaki, A., Furukawa, J., Tsuruta, T., Inoue, S. and Ito, K., *Makromol. Chem.*, **36**, 260 (1960).

134. Kawasaki, A., Furukawa, J., Tsuruta, T., Nakayama, Y. and Wasai, Go., *Makromol. Chem.*, **49**, 112 (1961).
135. Kawasaki, A., Furukawa, J., Tsuruta, T., Salgusa, T., Kakogawa, G. and Sakata, R., *Polymer*, **1**, 315 (1960).
136. Kawasaki, A., Furukawa, J., Tsuruta, T. and Shiotani, S., *Polymer*, **2**, 143 (1961).
137. Kawasaki, A., Furukawa, J., Tsuruta, T., Wasai, Go and Makimoto, T., *Makromol. Chem.*, **49**, 76 (1961).
138. Kawasaki, A., Shiotani, S., Furukawa, J. and Tsuruta, T., *Bull. Chem. Soc. Japan*, **32**, 1149 (1959).
139. Ketley, A. D. and Harvey, M. C., *J. Org. Chem.*, **26**, 4649 (1961).
140. Kimmer, W. and Schmalz, E. O., *Z. Anal. Chem.*, **170**, 132 (1959); *ibid.* **181**, 229 (1961); *Kautschuk Gummi*, **11**, 606 (1963).
141. King, G. and Wood, I., *Nature*, **195**, 1093 (1962).
142. Kinoshita, Y., *Makromol. Chem.*, **33**, 1 (1960).
143. Komaki, C., Ichishima, I., Kuratani, K., Miyazawa, T., Shimanouchi, T. and Mizushima, S., *Bull. Chem. Soc. Japan*, **28**, 330 (1955).
144. Konishi, A., *Bull. Chem. Soc. Japan*, **35**, 395 (1962).
145. Korotkov, A. A., Mitsengendler, C. P., Krasulina, V. N. and Volkova, L. A., *Polymer Sci. USSR*, **1**, 506 (1960).
146. Korotkov, A. A., Mitsengendler, C. P., Krasulina, V. N. and Volkova, L. A., *Vysokomolekul. Soedin*, **1**, 1319 (1959).
147. Kössler, I. and Vodehnal, J., *Collection Czech. Chem. Commun.*, **29**, 2419 (1964).
148. Kössler, I. and Vodehnal, J., *Polymer Letters*, **1**, 415 (1963).
149. Kreshkov, A. P., Mikhailenko, J. J. and Makinovitch, G. F., *Shurnal analit. Chim.*, **9**, 208 (1954).
150. Kriegsmann, H., *Z. Elektrochem.*, **64**, 541, 848 (1960); *ibid.*, **65**, 336 (1961).
151. Krimm, S., *Fortschr. Hochpolymer.-Forsch.*, **1**, 1, 51 (1960).
152. Krimm, S., *J. Polymer Sci.*, **61**, S 40 (1962).
153. Krimm, S., Berens, A. R., Folt, V. L. and Shipman, J. J., *Chem. Ind.* (London), **1958**, 1512; **1959**, 433.
154. Krimm, S. and Enomoto, S., *J. Polymer Sci.*, **A 2**, 669 (1964).
155. Krimm, S., Folt, V. L., Shipman, J. J. and Berens, A. R., *J. Polymer Sci.*, **A 1**, 2621 (1963).
156. Krimm, S. and Liang, C. Y., *J. Polymer Sci.*, **22**, 95 (1956).
157. Krimm, S., Liang, C. Y. and Sutherland, G. B. B. M., *J. Chem. Phys.*, **25**, 549 (1956).
158. Kuroda, Y. and Kubo, M., *J. Polymer Sci.*, **26**, 323 (1957).
159. Kuroda, Y. and Kubo, M., *J. Polymer Sci.*, **36**, 453 (1959).
160. Lancaster, J. E., Stamm, R. F. and Colthup, N. B., *Spectrochim. Acta*, **17**, 155 (1961).
161. Lebas, J. M., *J. Chim. Phys.*, **59**, 1072 (1962).
162. Lee, S. M. and Brelant, S., *Mod. Plastics*, **41**, 150 (1963).
163. Liang, C. Y., *J. Mol. Spectr.*, **1**, 61 (1957).
164. Liang, C. Y. and Krimm, S., *J. Chem. Phys.*, **25**, 563 (1956).
165. Liang, C. Y. and Krimm, S., *J. Mol. Spectr.*, **3**, 554 (1959).
166. Liang, C. Y. and Krimm, S., *J. Polymer Sci.*, **27**, 241 (1958).
167. Liang, C. Y. and Krimm, S., *J. Polymer Sci.*, **31**, 513 (1958).

168. Liang, C. Y., Krimm, S. and Sutherland, G. B. B. M., *J. Chem. Phys.*, **25**, 543 (1956).
169. Liang, C. Y. and Lytton, M. R., *J. Polymer Sci.*, **61**, S 45 (1962).
170. Liang, C. Y., Lytton, M. R. and Boone, C. J., *J. Polymer Sci.*, **44**, 549 (1960).
171. Liang, C. Y., Lytton, M. R. and Boone, C. J., *J. Polymer Sci.*, **47**, 139 (1960).
172. Laing, C. Y., Lytton, M. R. and Boone, C. J., *J. Polymer Sci.*, **54**, 523 (1961).
173. Liang, C. Y. and Pearson, F. G., *J. Mol. Spectr.*, **5**, 290 (1960).
174. Liang, C. Y. and Watt, W. R., *J. Polymer Sci.*, **51**, S 14 (1961).
175. Loshaek, S. and Fox, T. G., *J. Am. Chem. Soc.*, **75**, 3544 (1953).
176. Loughran, G. A., Ehlers, G. F. L., Crawford, W. J., Burkett, J. L. and Ray, J. D., *Appl. Spectr.*, **18**, 129 (1964).
177. Lucier, J. J. and Bentley, F. F., "The characterization of saturated aliphatic esters in the 15-40 micron region," 14th *Annual Mid-America Spectroscopy Symposium, May* 1963, *Chicago, Illinois.*
178. Luongo, J. P., *J. Appl. Polymer Sci.*, **3**, 302 (1960).
179. McBee, E. T., Hill, H. M. and Bachman, G. B., *Ind. Eng. Chem.*, **41**, 70 (1949).
180. McDonald, M. P. and Ward, I. M., *Polymer*, **2**, 341 (1961).
181. Marshall, H. W., "Development of an infrared, prism-grating, double beam recording spectrophotometer," *WADC Technical Report* 59-763, *Wright-Patterson Air Force Base, Ohio.*
182. Marvel, C. S., Sample, J. H. and Roy, M. F., *J. Am. Chem. Soc.*, **61**, 3241 (1939).
183. Matsubara, I., *Bull. Chem. Soc. Japan*, **33**, 1624 (1960).
184. Matsuo, H., *J. Polymer Sci.*, **21**, 331 (1956).
185. Matsuo, H., *J. Polymer Sci.*, **25**, 234 (1957).
186. May, L. and Schwing, K. J., *Appl. Spectr.*, **17**, 166 (1963).
187. Melville, H. W., Peaker, F. W. and Vale, R. L., *Makromol. Chem.*, **28**, 140 (1958).
188. Meyrick, C. I. and Thompson, H. W., *J. Chem. Soc.*, **1950**, 225.
189. Miller, M. L. and Rauhut, C. E., *J. Am. Chem. Soc.*, **80**, 4115 (1958).
190. Miller, M. L. and Rauhut, C. E., *J. Polymer Sci.*, **38**, 63 (1959).
191. Miller, R. G. J., Mills, B., Small, P., Turner-Jones, A. and Wood, D., *Chem. Ind.*, **1958**, 1323.
192. Miller, R. G. J. and Willis, H. A., *J. Polymer Sci.*, **19**, 485 (1956).
192a. Mirone, P., *Spectrochim. Acta*, **20**, 1646 (1964).
193. Miyake, A., *J. Am. Chem. Soc.*, **82**, 3040 (1960).
194. Miyake, A., *J. Polymer Sci.*, **38**, 479, 497 (1959).
195. Miyake, A., *J. Polymer Sci.*, **44**, 223 (1960).
196. Miyazawa, T., *J. Chem. Phys.*, **35**, 693 (1961).
197. Miyazawa, T., *J. Polymer Sci.*, C 7, 59 (1964).
198. Miyazawa, T., *Polymer Letters*, **2**, 847 (1964).
199. Miyazawa, T., Fukushima, K. and Ideguchi, Y., *J. Chem. Phys.*, **37**, 2764 (1962).
200. Miyazawa, T., Fukushima, K. and Ideguchi, Y., *Polymer Letters*, **1**, 385 (1963).
201. Miyazawa, T. and Ideguchi, Y., *Bull. Chem. Soc. Japan*, **36**, 1125 (1963).
202. Miyazawa, T. and Ideguchi, Y., *Bull. Chem. Soc. Japan*, **37**, 1065 (1964).

203. Miyazawa, T., Ideguchi, Y. and Fukushima, K., *J. Chem. Phys.*, **38**, 2709 (1963).
204. Miyazawa, T., Shimanouchi, T. and Mizushima, S., *J. Chem. Phys.*, **24**, 408 (1956); *ibid.*, **29**, 611 (1958).
205. Mizushima, S., Shimanouchi, T., Nakagawa, I. and Miyake, A., *J. Chem. Phys.*, **21**, 215 (1953).
206. Mizushima, S., Shimanouchi, T., Nakamura, K., Hayashi, M. and Tsuchiya, S., *J. Chem. Phys.*, **26**, 970 (1957).
207. Morero, D., Mantica, E., Ciampelli, F. and Sianesi, D., *Nuovo Cimento Suppl.*, **15**, 122 (1960).
208. Morero, D., Santambrogio, A., Porri, L. and Ciampelli, F., *Chim. Ind. (Milan)*, **41**, 758 (1959).
209. Mortimer, F., *Spectrochim. Acta*, **9**, 270 (1957).
210. Moynihan, R. E., *J. Am. Chem. Soc.*, **81**, 1045 (1959).
211. Murahashi, S., Nozakura, S. and Tadokoro, H., *Bull. Chem. Soc., Japan*, **32**, 534 (1959).
212. Nakagawa, I. and Mizushima, S., *J. Chem. Phys.*, **21**, 2195 (1953).
213. Nakamura, Y., *Kogyo Kagaku Zasshi*, **60**, 785 (1957); *ibid.*, **61**, 480 (1958).
214. Nakayama, Y., Tsuruta, T., Furukawa, J., Kawasaki, A. and Wasai, Go, *Makromol. Chem.*, **43**, 76 (1961).
215. Narita, S., Ichinohe, S. and Enomoto, S., *J. Polymer Sci.*, **36**, 389 (1959).
216. Narita, S., Ichinohe, S. and Enomoto, S., *J. Polymer Sci.*, **37**, 251, 263 (1959).
217. Narita, S., Ichinohe, S. and Enomoto, S., *J. Polymer Sci.*, **37**, 273, 281 (1959).
218. Narita, S. and Okuda, K., *J. Polymer Sci.*, **38**, 270 (1959).
219. Natta, G., *Makromol. Chem.*, **16**, 213 (1955).
220. Natta, G., Bassi, I. and Corradini, P., *Makromol. Chem.*, **18/19**, 455 (1956).
221. Natta, G. and Corradini, P., *Atti. Accad. Naz. Lincei Rend., Classe Sci. Fis., Mat. Nat.*, **18**, 19 (1955).
222. Natta, G., Corradini, P. and Bassi, I. W., *Makromol. Chem.*, **21**, 240 (1956).
223. Natta, G., Corradini, P., Sianesi, D. and Morero, D., *J. Polymer Sci.*, **51**, 527 (1961).
224. Natta, G., Dall'Asta, G., Mazzanti, G., Giannini, U. and Cesca, S., *Angew. Chem.*, **71**, 205 (1959).
225. Natta, G. and Pasquon, I., *Rubber Plastics Age*, **42**, 1939 (1961).
226. Natta, G., Pasquon, I., Corradini, P., Peraldo, M., Pegoraro, M. and Zambelli, A., *Atti. Acad. Naz. Lincei Rend., Classe Sci. Fis., Mat. Nat.*, **28**, 539 (1960).
227. Natta, G., Pasquon, I. and Zambelli, A., *J. Am. Chem. Soc.*, **84**, 1488 (1962).
228. Natta, G., Porri, L., Corradini, P. and Morero, D., *Atti. Accad. Naz. Lincei Rend., Classe Sci. Fis., Mat. Nat.*, **20**, 560 (1956).
229. Natta, G., Porri, L., Corradini, P. and Morero, D., *Chim. Ind. (Milan)*, **40**, 362 (1958).
230. Natta, G., Porri, L. and Mazzei, A., *Chim. Ind. (Milan)*, **41**, 116 (1959).
231. Natta, G., Porri, L., Mazzei, A. and Morero, D., *Chim. Ind. (Milan)*, **41**, 398 (1959).

232. Natta, G., Porri, L., Zanini, G. and Fiore, L., *Chim. Ind.* (*Milan*), **4i**, 526 (1959).

233. Nelson, K. V., *Dokl. Akad. Nauk SSSR*, **95**, 57 (1954).

234. Nielsen, J. Rud and Woollett, A. H., *J. Chem. Phys.*, **26**, 1391 (1957).

235. Nikitin, V. N., Volkova, L. A., Michailova, N. V. and Baklagina, J. U. G., *Vysokomolekul. Soedin*, **1**, 1094 (1959); *Polymer Sci.*, *USSR*, **1**, 406 (1960).

236. Nishioka, A., Watanabe, H., Abe, K. and Sono, Y., *J. Polymer Sci.*, **48**, 241 (1960).

237. Novak, A. and Whalley, E., *Can. J. Chem.*, **37**, 1710 (1959).

238. Novak, A. and Whalley, E., *Trans. Faraday Soc.*, **55**, 1484 (1959).

239. Nyquist, R. A., *Appl. Spectr.*, **11**, 161 (1957).

240. Nyquist, R. A., *Infrared Spectra of Plastics and Resins*, The Dow Chemical Company, Midland, Michigan (1961).

241. Onishi, T. and Krimm, S., *J. Appl. Phys.*, **32**, 2320 (1961).

242. Padden, F. J. and Keith, H. D., *J. Appl. Phys.*, **30**, 1479 (1959).

243. Padgett, W. M. and Hammer, W. F., *J. Am. Chem. Soc.*, **80**, 803 (1958).

244. Palm, A., *J. Phys. Chem.*, **55**, 1320 (1951).

245. Patterson, W. A., *Analyt. Chem.*, **26**, 823 (1954).

246. Peraldo, M., *Gazz. Chim. Ital.*, **89**, 798 (1959).

247. Petersen, H., *Angew. Chem.*, **76**, 909 (1964).

248. Pfann, H. F., Williams, V. Z. and Mark, H., *J. Polymer Sci.*, **1**, 14 (1946).

249. Pierce, R. H. H., Clark, E. S., Whitney, J. F. and Bryant, W. M. D. "Crystal structure of polytetrafluoroethylene"; *Am. Chem. Soc.*, 130*th* *Meeting, September*, 1956, Abstracts.

250. Pitzer, K. S. and Scott, D. H., *J. Am. Chem. Soc.*, **65**, 803 (1943).

251. Pokrovskii, E. I. and Kotova, I. P., *Soviet Phys.*, *Tech. Phys.* (*English Transl.*), **1**, 1417 (1957).

252. Pokrovskii, E. I. and Kotova, I. P., *Zh. Tekhn. Fiz.*, **26**, 1456 (1956).

253. Pokrovskii, E. I. and Wolkenstein, M. V., *Dokl. Akad. Nauk SSSR*, **95**, 301 (1954).

254. Pokrovskii, E. I. and Wolkenstein, M. V., *Izv. Akad. Nauk SSSR, Ser. Fiz.*, **23**, 1208 (1959).

255. Popov, E. M. and Kagan, G. I., *Opt. Spectry.* (*USSR*) (*English Transl.*), **12**, 102 (1962).

256. Price, C. C. and Osgan, M., *J. Am. Chem. Soc.*, **78**, 4787 (1956).

257. Price, C. C., Osgan, M., Hughes, R. E. and Shambelan, C., *J. Am. Chem. Soc.*, **78**, 690 (1956).

258. Prietzschk, A., *Kolloid-Z.*, **156**, 8 (1958).

259. Quynn, R. G., Riley, J. L., Young, D. A. and Noether, H. D., *J. Appl. Polymer Sci.*, **2**, 166 (1959).

260. Ramakrishnan, C. S., Dasgupta, S. and Pande, J. P., *J. Polymer Sci.*, **19**, 323 (1956).

261. Ramakrishnan, C. S., Dasgupta, S. and Rao, N. V. C., *Makromol. Chem.*, **20**, 46 (1956).

262. Randall, H. M., Dennison, D. M., Ginsburg, N. and Weber, L. R., *Phys. Rev.*, **52**, 160 (1937).

262a. Rao, K. N. *et al.*, *J. Opt. Soc. Am.*, **52**, 862 (1962).

263. Rasmussen, R. S. and Brattain, R. R., *J. Chem. Phys.*, **15**, 120 (1947).

264. Reed, C. E. and Favero, G. D., *Mod. Plastics.*, **46**, 102 (1963).
265. Reimschuessel, H. K. and McDevitt, N. T., *J. Am. Chem. Soc.*, **82**, 3756 (1960).
266. Reinhardt, R. C., *Ind. Eng. Chem.*, **35**, 422 (1943).
267. Richards, R. E. and Thompson, H. W., *J. Chem. Soc.*, **1947**, 1260.
268. Richards, R. E. and Thompson, H. W., *J. Chem. Soc.*, **1949**, 124.
269. Richardson, W. S. and Sacher, A., *J. Polymer Sci.*, **10**, 353 (1953).
270. Robinson, T. S. and Price, W. C., *Proc. Phys. Soc.*, *B*, **66**, 969 (1953).
271. Rohmer, M., *Angew. Chem.*, **71**, 459 (1959).
272. Rosenthal, A., Lederer, F. and Gilson, K., *Can. J. Chem.*, **34**, 679 (1956).
273. Rugg, F. M., Smith, J. J. and Wartman, L. H., *J. Polymer Sci.*, **11**, 1 (1953).
274. Salomon, G., Schooneveldt-van det Kloes, C. J. and Zwiers, J. H. L., *Rec. Trav. Chim.*, **79**, 313 (1960).
275. Salomon, G. and van der Schee, A. C., *J. Polymer Sci.*, **14**, 181 (1954).
276. Salomon, G. and van der Schee, A. C., *J. Polymer Sci.*, **14**, 287 (1954).
277. Sandeman, I. and Keller, A., *J. Polymer Sci.*, **19**, 401 (1956).
278. Saunders, R. A. and Smith, D. C., *J. Appl. Phys.*, **20**, 953 (1949).
279. Schildknecht, C. E., *Ind. Eng. Chem.*, **50**, 112 (1958).
280. Schildknecht, C. E., Gross, S. T., Davidson, H. R., Lambert, J. M. and Zoss, A. O., *Ind. Eng. Chem.*, **40**, 2104 (1948).
281. Schildknecht, C. E., Zoss, A. O. and McKinley, C., *Ind. Eng. Chem.*, **39**, 180 (1947).
282. Schmalz, E. O. and Geiseler, G., *Z. Anal. Chem.*, **190**, 293 (1962).
283. Schmalz, E. O. and Geiseler, G., *Z. Anal. Chem.*, **191** (1962).
284. Schmidt, P. and Schneider, B., *Collection Czech. Chem. Commun.*, **28**, 2685 (1963).
285. Schmidt, P. G., *J. Polymer Sci.*, **A 1**, 2317 (1963).
286. Schmidt, P. G. and Gay, F. P., *Angew. Chem.*, **74**, 638 (1962).
287. Schneider, B., Schmidt, P. and Wichterle, O., *Collection Czech. Chem. Commun.*, **27**, 1749 (1962).
288. Schneider, C., Herz, J. and Hummel, D., *Makromol. Chem.*, **56**, 228 (1962); *ibid.*, **73**, 128 (1964).
289. Schnell, G., *Ergeb. Exakt. Naturw.*, **31**, 270 (1959).
290. Schooten, J. van and Mostert, S., *Polymer*, **4**, 135 (1963).
291. Schurz, J., Bayzer, H. and Stübchen, H., *Makromol. Chem.*, **23**, 152 (1957).
292. Seifert, H. S. and Randall, H. M., *Rev. Sci. Instr.*, **11**, 365 (1960).
293. Semon, W. L. and Craig, D., *Rubber and Plastics Age*, **40**, 140 (1959); *Rev. Gen. Caoutchuc.*, **35**, 1227 (1958); *Kautschuk Gummi*, **11**, WT 207 (1958).
294. Semon, W. L., Craig, D., Fowler, R., Regenass, F., Tucker, H., Yanko, J., Shipman, J. and Belt, R., *Science*, **128**, 359 (1958).
295. Sheppard, N., *J. Chem. Phys.*, **17**, 74 (1949).
296. Sheppard, N., *Trans. Faraday Soc.*, **46**, 527, 533 (1950).
297. Sheppard, N. and Sutherland, G. B. B. M., *Proc. Roy. Soc.* (*London*), *Ser. A*, 196, 195 (1949).
298. Shigorin, D. H., Mikhailov, N. V. and Makareva, S. P., *Dokl. Akad. Nauk SSSR*, **97**, 711 (1954).
299. Shimanouchi, T., Kakiuti, Y. and Gamo, I., *J. Chem. Phys.*, **25**, 1245 (1956).
300. Shimanouchi, T. and Tasumi, M., *Spectrochim. Acta*, **17**, 755 (1961).

301. Shimanouchi, T., Tsuchiya, S. and Mizushima, S., *J. Chem. Phys.*, **30**, 1365 (1959).
302. Shimanouchi, T., Tsuchiya, S. and Mizushima, S., *Kobunshi Kagaku*, **8**, 202 (1959).
303. Shreve, O. D., Heether, M. R., Knight, H. B. and Swern, D., *Anal. Chem.*, **23**, 277 (1951).
304. Sibilia, J. P. and Wincklhofer, R. C., *J. Appl. Polymer Sci.*, **6**, S 56 (1962).
305. Signer, R. and Weiler, J., *Helv. Chim. Acta*, **15**, 649 (1932).
306. Silas, R. S., Yates, J. and Thornton, V., *Anal. Chem.*, **31**, 529 (1959).
307. Simon, A., Mücklich, M., Kunath, D. and Heinz, G., *J. Polymer Sci.*, **30**, 201 (1958).
308. Smith, A. Lee, *Spectrochim. Acta.*, **19**, 849 (1963).
309. Smith, A. Lee, Brown, L. H., Tyler, L. J. and Hunter, M. J., *Ind. Eng. Chem.*, **49**, 1903 (1957).
310. Smith, A. Lee and McHard, J. A., *Anal. Chem.*, **31**, 1174 (1959).
311. Smook, M. A., Pieski, E. T. and Hammer, C. F., *Ind. Eng. Chem.*, **45**, 2731 (1953).
312. Soda, R., *Bull. Chem. Soc. Japan*, **35**, 152 (1962).
313. Spurr, R. A., Hanking, B. M. and Rowen, I. W., *Polymer Sci.*, **37**, 431 (1959).
314. Stanevich, A. E. and Yaroslavsky, N. G., *Opt. Spectry. (USSR) (English Transl.)*, **11**, 31 (1961).
315. Starkweather, H. W. and Moynihan, R. E., *J. Polymer Sci.*, **22**, 363 (1956).
316. Stavely, F. W. *et al.*, *Ind. Eng. Chem.*, **48**, 778 (1956).
317. Stolka, M., Vodehnal, J. and Kössler, I., *Collection Czech. Chem. Commun.*, **28**, 1535 (1963).
318. Stromberg, R. R., Straus, S. and Achhammer, B. G., *J. Res. Nat. Bur. Std. A*, **60**, 147 (1958).
319. Stroupe, J. D. and Hughes, R. E., *J. Am. Chem. Soc.*, **80**, 2341 (1958).
320. Sutherland, G. B. B. M. and Jones, A. V., *Discussions Faraday Soc.*, **9**, 281 (1950).
321. Tadokoro, H., *J. Chem. Phys.*, **33**, 1558 (1960); *ibid.*, **35**, 1050 (1961).
322. Tadokoro, H., Kitazawa, T., Nozakura, S. and Murahashi, S., *Bull. Chem. Soc. Japan*, **34**, 1209 (1961).
323. Tadokoro, H., Kobayashi, M., Kawaguchi, Y., Kobayashi, A. and Murahashi, S., *J. Chem. Phys.*, **38**, 703 (1963).
324. Tadokoro, H., Kobayashi, A., Kawaguchi, Y., Sabajima, S. and Murahashi, S., *J. Chem. Phys.*, **35**, 369 (1961).
325. Tadokoro, H., Kobayashi, M., Murahashi, S., Mitsuishi, A. and Yoshinaga, H., *Bull. Chem. Soc. Japan*, **35**, 1429 (1962).
326. Tadokoro, H., Nishiyama, Y., Nozakura, S. and Murahashi, S., *Bull. Chem. Soc. Japan*, **34**, 381 (1960).
327. Tadokoro, H., Nishiyama, N., Nozakura, S. and Murahashi, S., *J. Polymer Sci.*, **36**, 553 (1959).
328. Tadokoro, H., Nozakura, S., Kitazawa, T., Yasuhara, Y. and Murahashi, S., *Bull. Chem. Soc. Japan*, **32**, 313 (1959).
329. Tadokoro, H., Tatsuka, K. and Murahashi, S., *J. Polymer Sci.*, **59**, 413 (1962).

330. Takeda, M. and Iimura, K., *J. Polymer Sci.*, **57**, 383 (1962).
331. Takeda, M., Iimura, K., Yamada, A. and Imamura, Y., *Bull. Chem. Soc. Japan*, **32**, 1150 (1959); *ibid.*, **33**, 1219 (1960).
332. Tasumi, M. and Shimanouchi, T., *Spectrochim. Acta*, **17**, 731 (1961).
333. Teyssié, P. and Smets, G., *J. Polymer Sci.*, **27**, 441 (1958).
334. Thompson, H. W. and Torkington, P., *J. Chem. Soc.*, **1945**, 640.
335. Thompson, H. W. and Torkington, P., *Proc. Roy. Soc. (London), Ser. A*, **184**, 3 (1945).
336. Thompson, H. W. and Torkington, P., *Proc. Roy. Soc. (London), Ser. A*, **184**, 21 (1945).
337. Thompson, H. W. and Torkington, P., *Trans. Faraday Soc.*, **41**, 246 (1945).
338. Tkač, A. and Kello, V., *Rubber Chem. Technol.*, **28**, 968 (1955).
339. Tobin, M. C., *J. Chem. Phys.*, **23**, 891 (1955).
340. Tobin, M. C., *J. Phys. Chem.*, **61**, 1392 (1957).
341. Tobin, M. C., *J. Phys. Chem.*, **64**, 216 (1960).
342. Tobin, M. C. and Carrano, M. J., *J. Chem. Phys.*, **25**, 1044 (1956).
343. Vodehnal, J. and Kössler, I., *Collection Czech. Chem. Commun.*, **29**, 2428 (1964).
344. Vodehnal, J. and Kössler, I., *Collection Czech. Chem. Commun.*, **29**, 2859 (1964).
345. Volchek, B. Z. and Nikitin, V. N., *Soviet Phys.-Tech. Phys. (English Transl.)*, **2**, 1705 (1957).
346. Ward, I. M., *Textile Res. J.*, **31**, 650 (1961).
347. Whiffen, D. H., *Spectrochim. Acta*, **7**, 253 (1955).
348. Wiberley, S. E. and Gonzalez, R. D., *Appl. Spectry.*, **15**, 174 (1961).
349. Wilke, G., *Angew. Chem.*, **68**, 306 (1956).
350. Willbourn, A. H., *J. Polymer Sci.*, **34**, 569 (1959).
351. Willis, H. A., Miller, Q. C. J., Adams, D. M. and Gebbie, H. A., *Spectrochim. Acta*, **19**, 1457 (1963).
352. Wilmshurst, J. K., *J. Chem. Phys.*, **25**, 1171 (1956).
353. Wood, D. L. and Luongo, J. P., *Mod. Plastics.*, **38**, 132 (March, 1961).
354. Wright, N. and Hunter, M. J., *J. Chem. Soc.*, **69**, 803 (1947).
355. Wyss, H. R., Werder, R. D. and Günthard, H. H., *Spectrochim. Acta*, **20**, 573 (1964).
356. Yamadera, R., *J. Polymer Sci.*, **50**, S 4 (1961).
357. Young, C. W., DuVall, R. B. and Wright, N., *Anal. Chem.*, **23**, 709 (1951).
358. Young, C. W., Servais, P. C., Currie, C. C. and Hunter, M. J., *J. Am. Chem. Soc.*, **70**, 3758 (1948).
359. Ziabicki, A., *Kolloid-Z.*, **167**, 132 (1959).

Appendix A

COLLECTION OF SPECTRA OF
HIGH POLYMERS, RESINS,
AND RELATED SUBSTANCES IN
THE 2–15 μ, AND IN THE
700–250 CM^{-1} REGION

1

FIR spectrum from 500 cm^{-1} to 250 cm^{-1} of water vapor

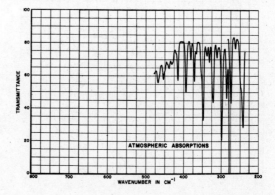

2

FIR spectrum from 700 cm^{-1} to 250 cm^{-1} of a cesium bromide plate

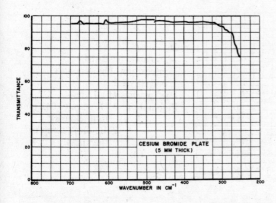

91

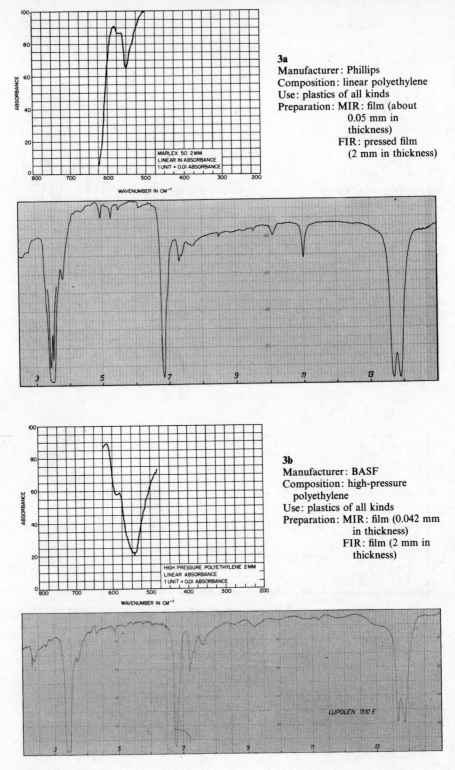

3a
Manufacturer: Phillips
Composition: linear polyethylene
Use: plastics of all kinds
Preparation: MIR: film (about
0.05 mm in
thickness)
FIR: pressed film
(2 mm in thickness)

MARLEX 50 2MM
LINEAR IN ABSORBANCE
1 UNIT = 0.01 ABSORBANCE

WAVENUMBER IN CM⁻¹

3b
Manufacturer: BASF
Composition: high-pressure
polyethylene
Use: plastics of all kinds
Preparation: MIR: film (0.042 mm
in thickness)
FIR: film (2 mm in
thickness)

HIGH PRESSURE POLYETHYLENE 2MM
LINEAR ABSORBANCE
1 UNIT = 0.01 ABSORBANCE

WAVENUMBER IN CM⁻¹

LUPOLEN 1810 E

92

4

Manufacturer: laboratory
  preparation (cationic)
Composition: atactic polypropylene,
  liquid
Preparation: liquid film

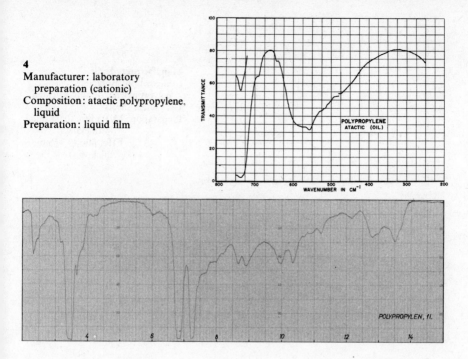

POLYPROPYLENE
ATACTIC (OIL)

POLYPROPYLEN, fl.

5

Manufacturer: laboratory
  preparation
Composition: partly isotactic
  polypropylene (amorphous,
  rubber-like)
Preparation: MIR: film from
              CHCl₃ solution
         FIR: pressed sheet

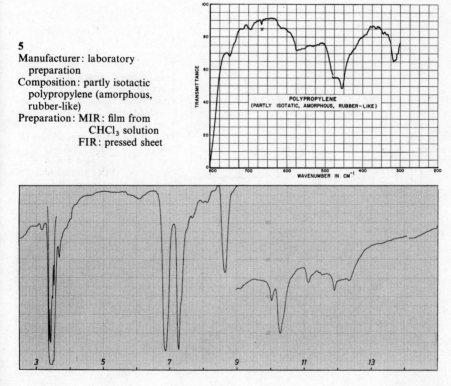

POLYPROPYLENE
(PARTLY ISOTATIC, AMORPHOUS, RUBBER-LIKE)

93

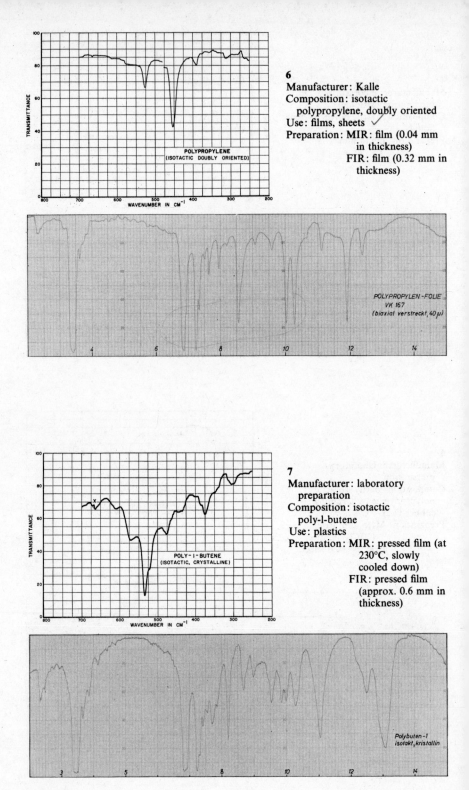

6
Manufacturer: Kalle
Composition: isotactic
  polypropylene, doubly oriented
Use: films, sheets ✓
Preparation: MIR: film (0.04 mm
    in thickness)
  FIR: film (0.32 mm in
    thickness)

POLYPROPYLENE
(ISOTACTIC DOUBLY ORIENTED)

POLYPROPYLEN-FOLIE
VK 167
(biaxial verstreckt, 40 μ)

7
Manufacturer: laboratory
  preparation
Composition: isotactic
  poly-1-butene
Use: plastics
Preparation: MIR: pressed film (at
    230°C, slowly
    cooled down)
  FIR: pressed film
    (approx. 0.6 mm in
    thickness)

POLY-1-BUTENE
(ISOTACTIC, CRYSTALLINE)

Polybuten-1
isotakt, kristallin

94

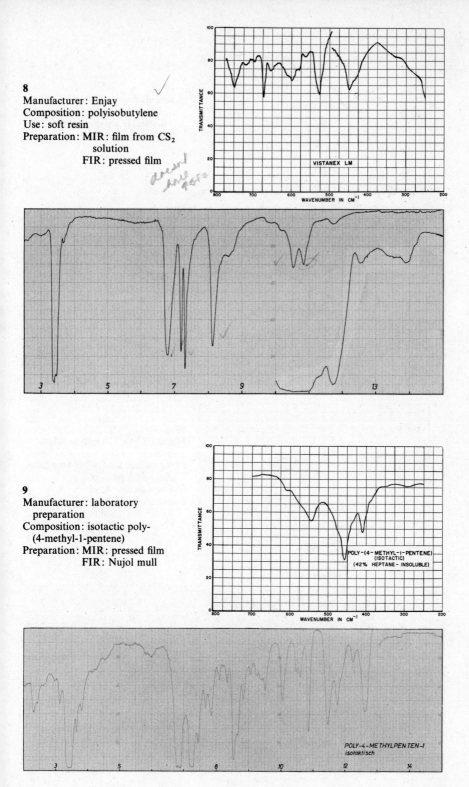

8

Manufacturer: Enjay
Composition: polyisobutylene
Use: soft resin
Preparation: MIR: film from CS_2
          solution
        FIR: pressed film

VISTANEX LM

9

Manufacturer: laboratory
   preparation
Composition: isotactic poly-
(4-methyl-1-pentene)
Preparation: MIR: pressed film
        FIR: Nujol mull

POLY-(4-METHYL-1-PENTENE)
(ISOTACTIC)
(42% HEPTANE-INSOLUBLE)

POLY-4-METHYLPENTEN-1
isotaktisch

95

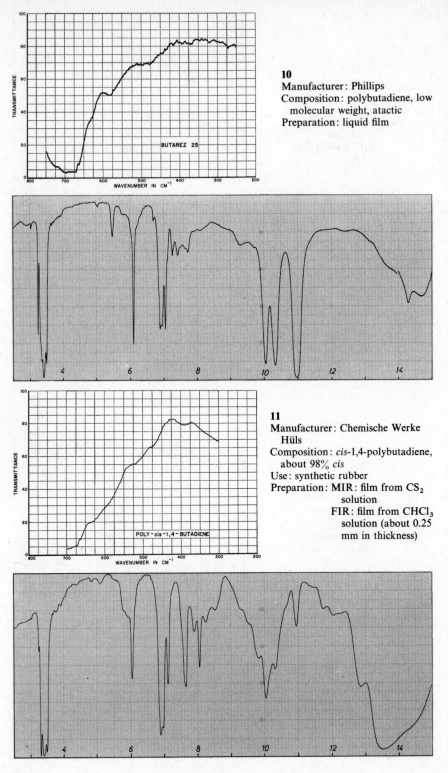

10
Manufacturer: Phillips
Composition: polybutadiene, low
  molecular weight, atactic
Preparation: liquid film

BUTAREZ 25

11
Manufacturer: Chemische Werke
  Hüls
Composition: *cis*-1,4-polybutadiene,
  about 98% *cis*
Use: synthetic rubber
Preparation: MIR: film from CS_2
              solution
            FIR: film from $CHCl_3$
              solution (about 0.25
              mm in thickness)

POLY - cis -1,4 - BUTADIENE

12

Manufacturer: Chemische Werke
  Hüls
Composition: *trans*-1,4-polybutadiene,
  crystalline, about 99 % *trans*
Preparation: MIR: film from CS_2
            solution
        FIR: film from $CHCl_3$
            solution (about 0.25
            mm in thickness)

13

Manufacturer: Goodrich
Composition: butadiene–
  acrylonitrile copolymer 70:30
Use: synthetic rubber
Preparation: MIR: film from
         CH_2Cl_2 dispersion
         (vibrating mill)
        FIR: pressed film
         (about 0.16 mm in
         thickness)

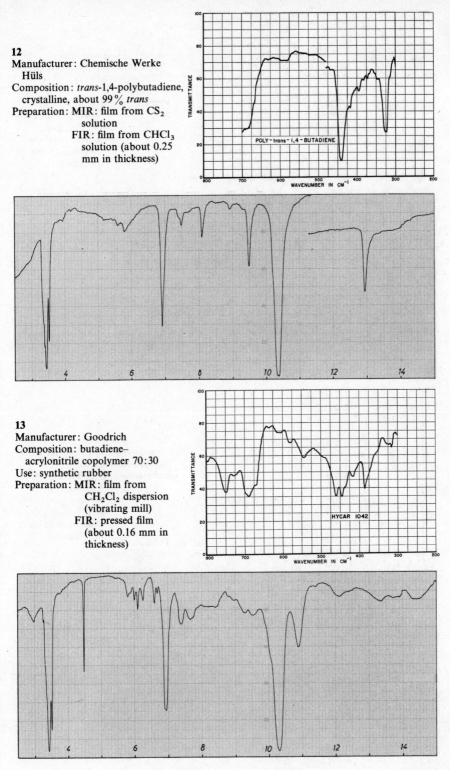

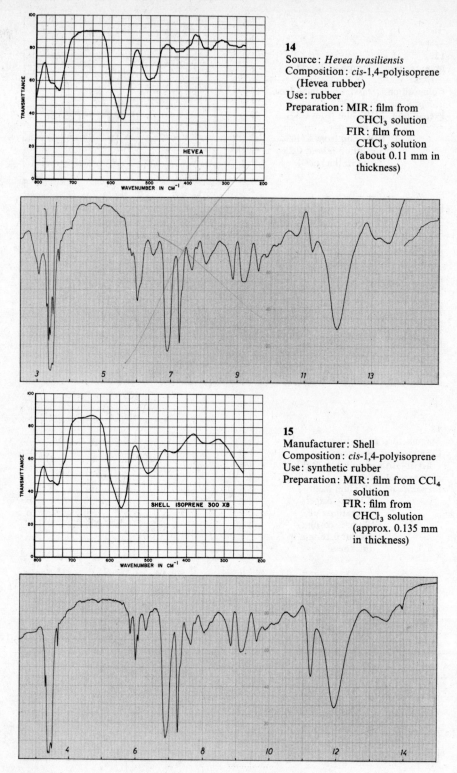

14
Source: *Hevea brasiliensis*
Composition: *cis*-1,4-polyisoprene
 (Hevea rubber)
Use: rubber
Preparation: MIR: film from
  CHCl₃ solution
 FIR: film from
  CHCl₃ solution
  (about 0.11 mm in
  thickness)

HEVEA

SHELL ISOPRENE 300 XB

15
Manufacturer: Shell
Composition: *cis*-1,4-polyisoprene
Use: synthetic rubber
Preparation: MIR: film from CCl₄
  solution
 FIR: film from
  CHCl₃ solution
  (approx. 0.135 mm
  in thickness)

16

Source: natural

Composition: *trans*-1,4-polyisoprene isoprene, crystalline

Use: thermoplastic material

Preparation: film from CHCl₃ solution

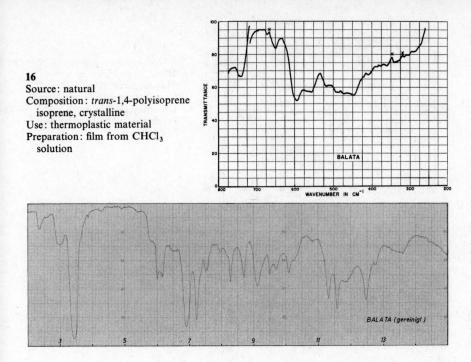

BALATA

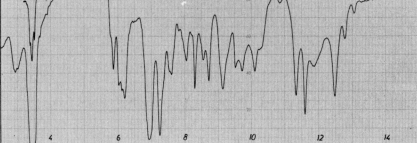

BALATA (gereinigt)

17

Source: natural

Composition: *trans*-1,4-polyisoprene isoprene, crystalline

Use: thermoplastic material

Preparation: MIR: film from CCl₄ solution
FIR: film from CHCl₃ solution

GUTTA PERCHA (PURIFIED)

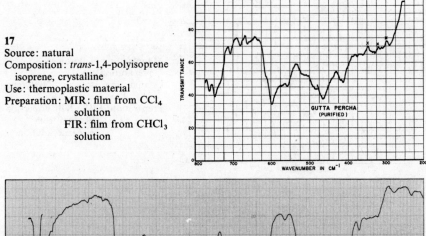

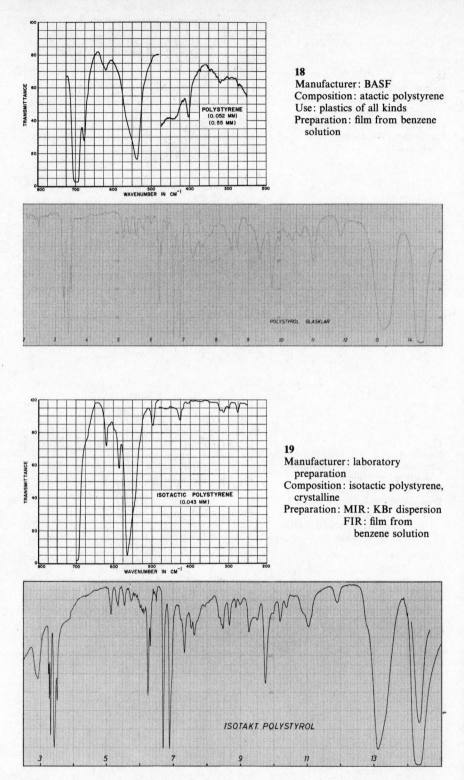

18
Manufacturer: BASF
Composition: atactic polystyrene
Use: plastics of all kinds
Preparation: film from benzene
solution

POLYSTYRENE
(0.052 MM)
(0.55 MM)

POLYSTYROL GLASKLAR

19
Manufacturer: laboratory
preparation
Composition: isotactic polystyrene,
crystalline
Preparation: MIR: KBr dispersion
FIR: film from
benzene solution

ISOTACTIC POLYSTYRENE
(0.043 MM)

ISOTAKT. POLYSTYROL

20

Manufacturer: Dow
Composition: Styrene–methyl
  methacrylate copolymer 50:50
Use: transparent thermoplastic
  material
Preparation: MIR: melted film
          FIR: film from CHCl₃
            solution (approx.
            0.085 mm in
            thickness)

21

Manufacturer: laboratory
  preparation
Composition: poly-α-methylstyrene
Preparation: film from CHCl₃
  solution

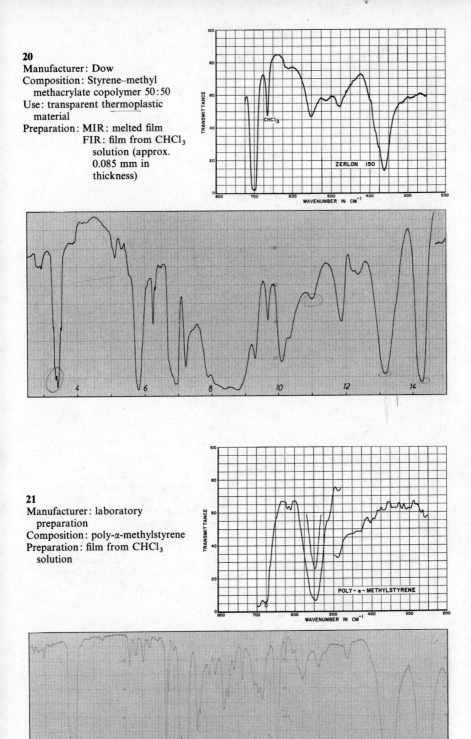

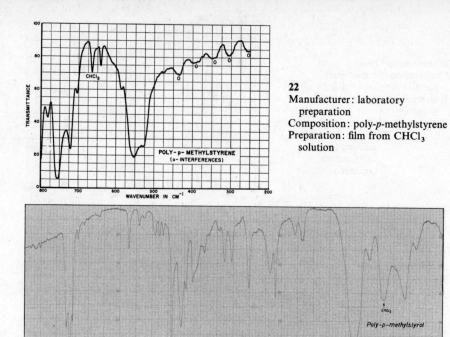

22

Manufacturer: laboratory
preparation
Composition: poly-*p*-methylstyrene
Preparation: film from $CHCl_3$
solution

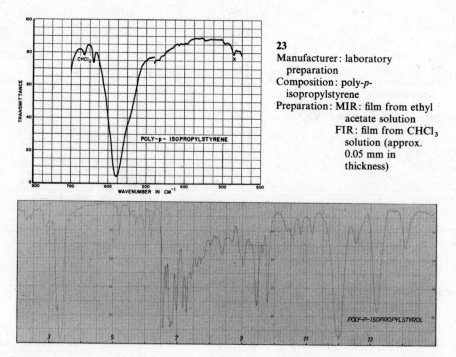

23

Manufacturer: laboratory
preparation
Composition: poly-*p*-
isopropylstyrene
Preparation: MIR: film from ethyl
acetate solution
FIR: film from $CHCl_3$
solution (approx.
0.05 mm in
thickness)

24

Manufacturer: American Cyanamid (FIR)
           laboratory preparation (MIR)
Composition: vinyltoluene–acrylonitrile copolymer 70:30
Use: transparent thermoplastic material
Preparation: MIR: film from CHCl₃ solution
        FIR: film from CHCl₃ solution (approx. 0.15 mm in thickness)

25

Manufacturer: Vereinigung für Teererzeugnisse
Composition: polyindene
Use: surface coating resin
Preparation: MIR: KBr dispersion
        FIR: film from CHCl₃ solution

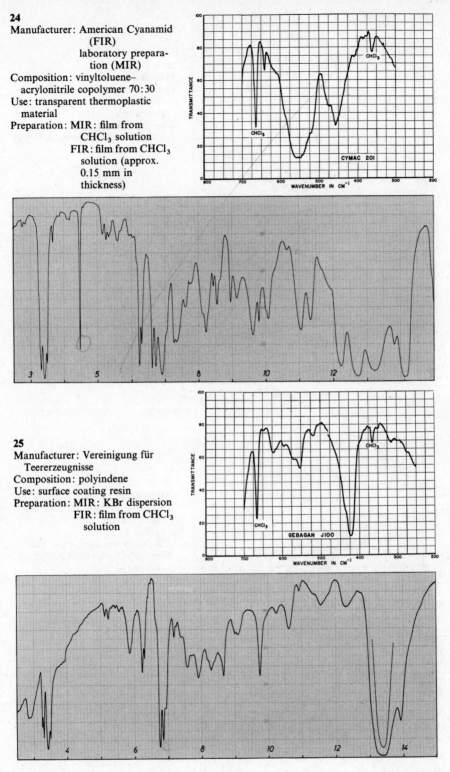

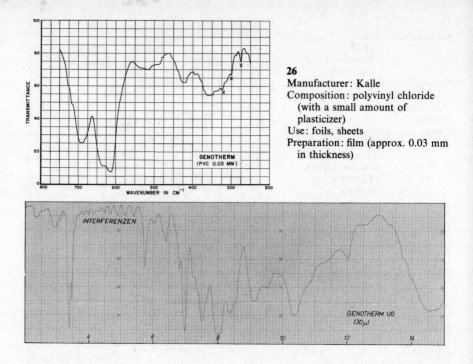

26

Manufacturer: Kalle
Composition: polyvinyl chloride
(with a small amount of
plasticizer)
Use: foils, sheets
Preparation: film (approx. 0.03 mm
in thickness)

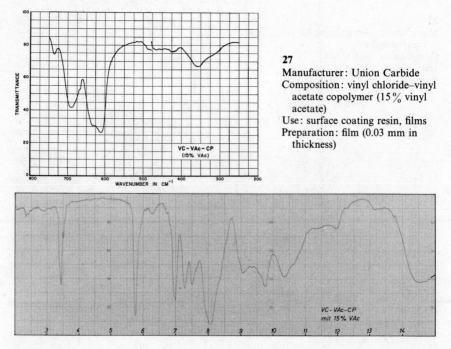

27

Manufacturer: Union Carbide
Composition: vinyl chloride–vinyl
acetate copolymer (15% vinyl
acetate)
Use: surface coating resin, films
Preparation: film (0.03 mm in
thickness)

28

Manufacturer: Dow
Composition: vinylidene chloride–
   vinyl chloride copolymer with an
   ester-type plasticizer
Use: films, surface coatings
Preparation: film (0.025 mm in
   thickness)

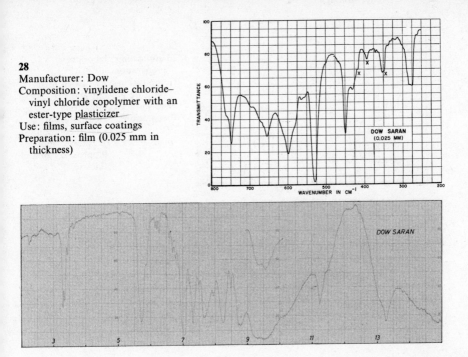

29

Manufacturer: Esso
Composition: low-chlorinated
   polyisobutene
Use: synthetic rubber
Preparation: MIR: film from
             kerosene solution
          FIR: pressed film

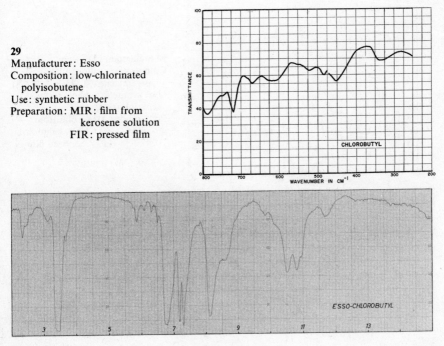

105

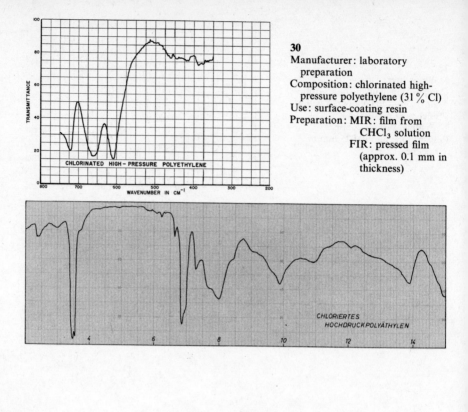

CHLORINATED HIGH-PRESSURE POLYETHYLENE

CHLORIERTES
HOCHDRUCKPOLYÄTHYLEN

30
Manufacturer: laboratory
    preparation
Composition: chlorinated high-
    pressure polyethylene (31 % Cl)
Use: surface-coating resin
Preparation: MIR: film from
          CHCl$_3$ solution
       FIR: pressed film
       (approx. 0.1 mm in
       thickness)

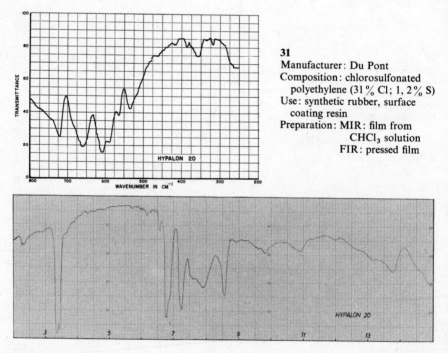

HYPALON 20

HYPALON 20

31
Manufacturer: Du Pont
Composition: chlorosulfonated
    polyethylene (31 % Cl; 1, 2 % S)
Use: synthetic rubber, surface
    coating resin
Preparation: MIR: film from
          CHCl$_3$ solution
       FIR: pressed film

32

Manufacturer: Kalle
Composition: rubber hydrochloride
   with some ester-type plasticizer
Use: films
Preparation: MIR: film (approx.
   0.02 mm in
   thickness)
   FIR: film (approx.
   0.04 mm in
   thickness)

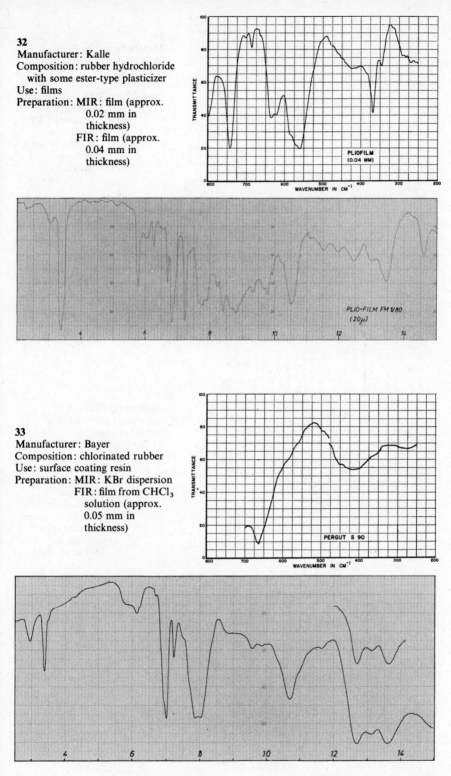

PLIOFILM
(0.04 MM)

PLIO-FILM FM 1/80
(20μ)

33

Manufacturer: Bayer
Composition: chlorinated rubber
Use: surface coating resin
Preparation: MIR: KBr dispersion
   FIR: film from $CHCl_3$
   solution (approx.
   0.05 mm in
   thickness)

PERGUT S 90

107

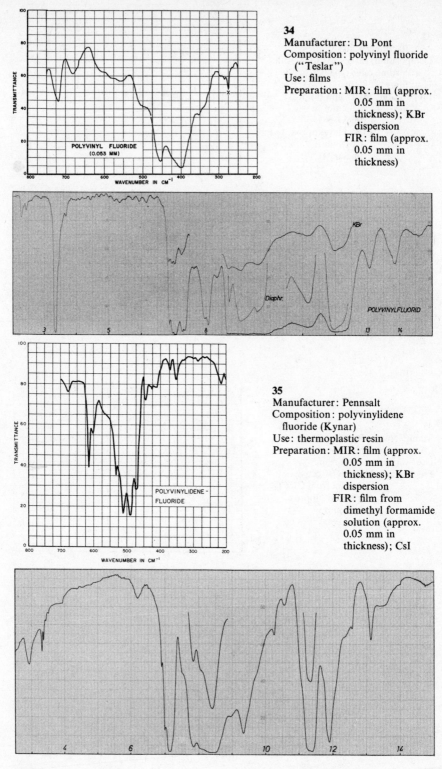

34

Manufacturer: Du Pont
Composition: polyvinyl fluoride
("Teslar")
Use: films
Preparation: MIR: film (approx.
0.05 mm in
thickness); KBr
dispersion
FIR: film (approx.
0.05 mm in
thickness)

POLYVINYL FLUORIDE
(0.053 MM)

KBr

Diaphr.

POLYVINYLFLUORID

35

Manufacturer: Pennsalt
Composition: polyvinylidene
fluoride (Kynar)
Use: thermoplastic resin
Preparation: MIR: film (approx.
0.05 mm in
thickness); KBr
dispersion
FIR: film from
dimethyl formamide
solution (approx.
0.05 mm in
thickness); CsI

POLYVINYLIDENE-
FLUORIDE

36

Manufacturer: Farbwerke Hoechst
Composition: polytetrafluoroethylene
Use: high-temperature material
Preparation: MIR: film (approx.
 0.04 mm in
 thickness); KBr
 dispersion
 FIR: film (approx.
 0.008 mm in
 thickness); KBr
 dispersion

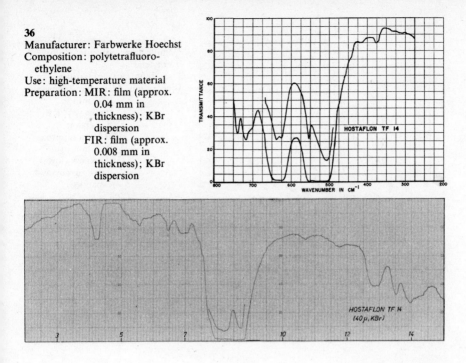

HOSTAFLON TF 14

HOSTAFLON TF 14
(40 µ, KBr)

37

Manufacturer: Minnesota Mining
 & Mfg. Co.
Composition: chlorotrifluoro-
 ethylene–vinylidene fluoride
 copolymer
Use: synthetic rubber, surface
 coating resin
Preparation: MIR: film (stretched);
 KBr dispersion
 FIR: film (approx.
 0.04 mm in
 thickness)

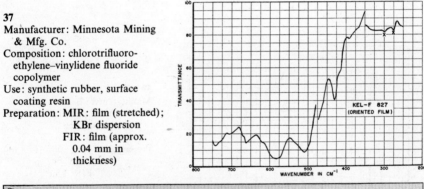

KEL-F 827
(ORIENTED FILM)

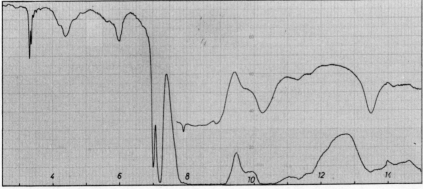

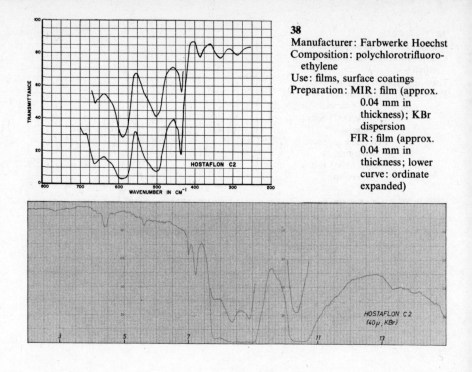

38
Manufacturer: Farbwerke Hoechst
Composition: polychlorotrifluoroethylene
Use: films, surface coatings
Preparation: MIR: film (approx.
0.04 mm in
thickness); KBr
dispersion
FIR: film (approx.
0.04 mm in
thickness; lower
curve: ordinate
expanded)

HOSTAFLON C2

HOSTAFLON C2
(40μ, KBr)

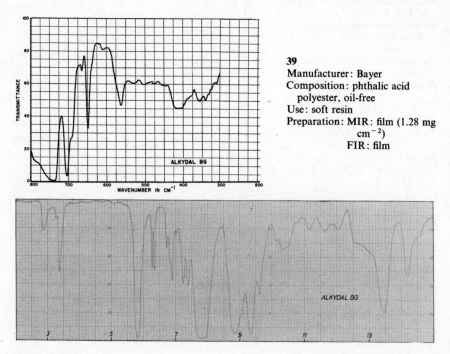

39
Manufacturer: Bayer
Composition: phthalic acid
polyester, oil-free
Use: soft resin
Preparation: MIR: film (1.28 mg
cm^{-2})
FIR: film

ALKYDAL BG

ALKYDAL BG

110

40

Manufacturer: American Cyanamid
Co.
Composition: diallyl phthalate
prepolymer
Use: unsaturated polyester resin
Preparation: MIR: KBr dispersion
FIR: film from
CHCl₃ solution

41

Manufacturer: Chemische Werke
Albert
Composition: coconut alkyd
(42% oil)
Use: surface coating resin
Preparation: MIR: film (1.63 mg
cm⁻²)
FIR: film

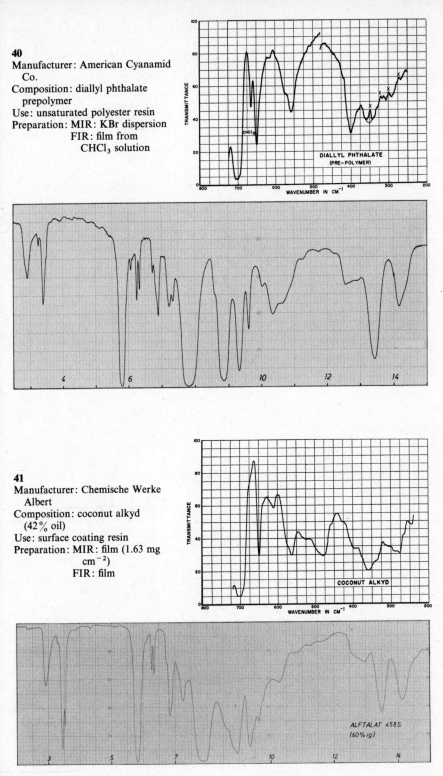

DIALLYL PHTHALATE
(PRE-POLYMER)

COCONUT ALKYD

ALFTALAT 458S
(60% ig)

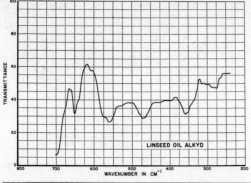

LINSEED OIL ALKYD

42
Manufacturer: Jäger
Composition: linseed oil alkyd
Use: surface coating resin
Preparation: film

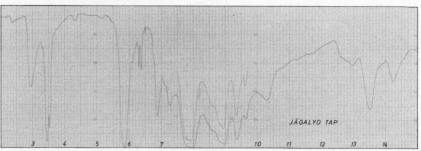

JÄGALYD TAP

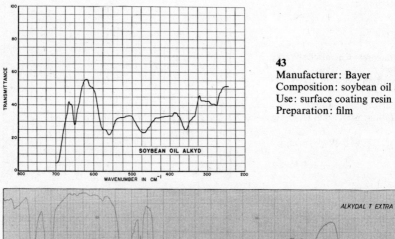

SOYBEAN OIL ALKYD

43
Manufacturer: Bayer
Composition: soybean oil alkyd
Use: surface coating resin
Preparation: film

ALKYDAL T EXTRA

44

Manufacturer: Bergvik
Composition: tall oil alkyd (80 %
　tall oil)
Use: surface coating resin
Preparation: MIR: film (2.02 mg
　　　　　　cm^{-2})
　　　　FIR: film

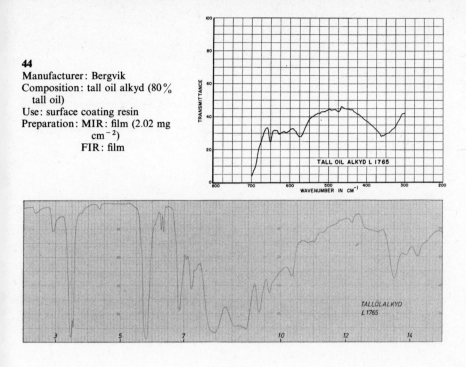

TALL OIL ALKYD L 1765

TALLÖLALKYD
L 1765

45

Manufacturer: Union Carbide
Composition: epoxy-modified
　dehydrated Castor oil
Use: stabilizer, plasticizer
Preparation: film

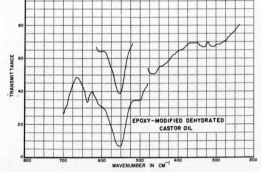

EPOXY−MODIFIED DEHYDRATED
CASTOR OIL

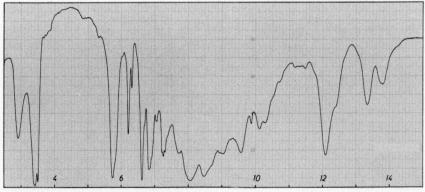

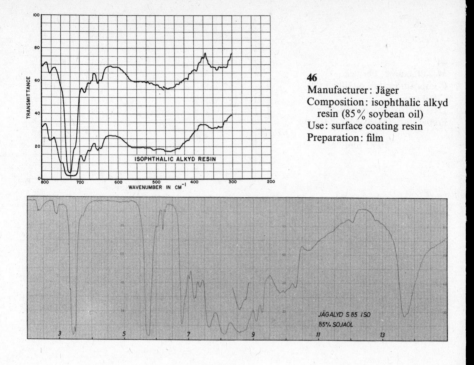

ISOPHTHALIC ALKYD RESIN

46

Manufacturer: Jäger
Composition: isophthalic alkyd
  resin (85% soybean oil)
Use: surface coating resin
Preparation: film

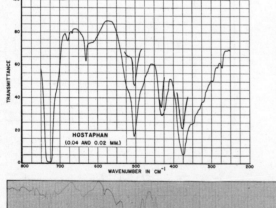

JÄGALYD S 85 ISO
85% SOJAÖL

47

Manufacturer: Kalle
Composition: ethylene glycol–
  terephthalic acid polyester,
  crystalline
Use: films, fibers
Preparation: MIR: film (approx.
    0.005–0.01 mm in
    thickness)
  FIR: film (approx.
    0.04 and 0.02 mm
    in thickness)

HOSTAPHAN
(0.04 AND 0.02 MM.)

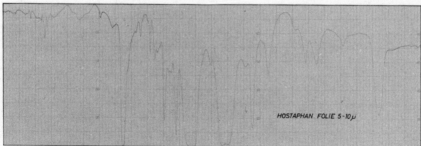

HOSTAPHAN FOLIE 5-10μ

48
Manufacturer: Dr Beck & Co.
Composition: terephthalic acid
  polyester, amorphous
Use: wire enamel
Preparation: film

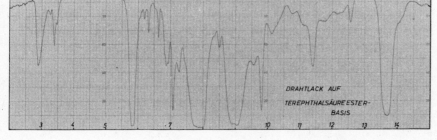

49
Manufacturer: Bayer
Composition: styrenated alkyd
  resin
Use: surface coating resin
Preparation: MIR: film (3.55 mg
              cm^{-2})
          FIR: film (approx.
              0.11 mm in
              thickness)

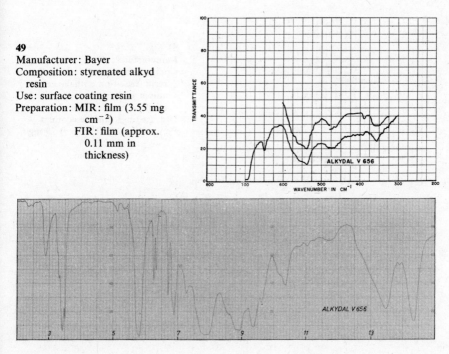

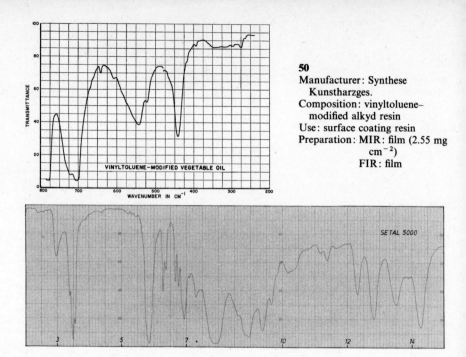

VINYLTOLUENE-MODIFIED VEGETABLE OIL

SETAL 5000

50
Manufacturer: Synthese
 Kunstharzges.
Composition: vinyltoluene–
 modified alkyd resin
Use: surface coating resin
Preparation: MIR: film (2.55 mg
 cm^{-2})
 FIR: film

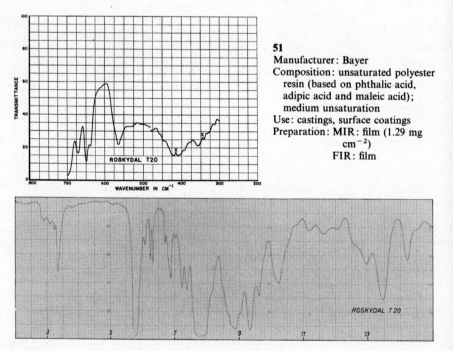

ROSKYDAL T20

ROSKYDAL T 20

51
Manufacturer: Bayer
Composition: unsaturated polyester
 resin (based on phthalic acid,
 adipic acid and maleic acid);
 medium unsaturation
Use: castings, surface coatings
Preparation: MIR: film (1.29 mg
 cm^{-2})
 FIR: film

116

52

Manufacturer: Bayer
Composition: unsaturated polyester
   resin (based on phthalic acid,
   adipic acid and maleic acid);
   high unsaturation
Use: surface coatings
Preparation: MIR: film (1.35 mg
          cm^{-2})
      FIR: film

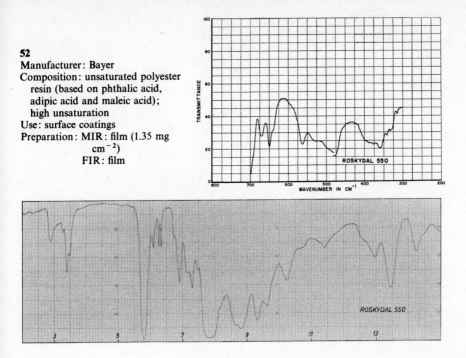

ROSKYDAL 550

53

Manufacturer: Bayer
Composition: polycarbonate based
   on 4,4′-dihydroxydiphenyl-
   propane ("bisphenol A")
Use: films, transparent plastics
Preparation: film (0.023 mm in
   thickness)

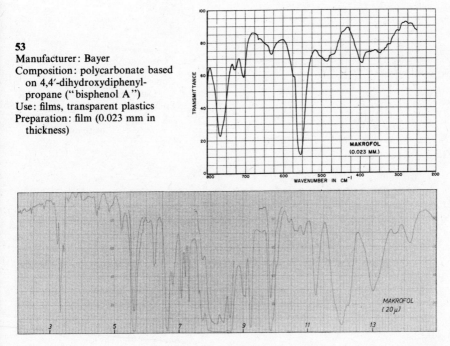

MAKROFOL
(0.023 MM.)

MAKROFOL
(20μ)

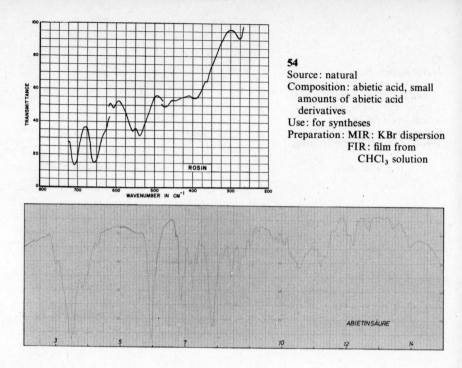

ROSIN

54
Source: natural
Composition: abietic acid, small
  amounts of abietic acid
  derivatives
Use: for syntheses
Preparation: MIR: KBr dispersion
    FIR: film from
      CHCl₃ solution

ABIETINSÄURE

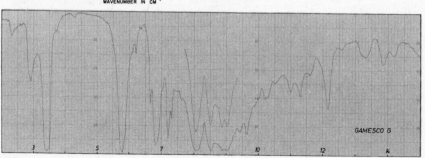

ROSIN GLYCERYL ESTER

55
Manufacturer: Masereel
Composition: rosin glyceryl ester
Use: soft resin for surface coatings
Preparation: MIR: KBr dispersions
    FIR: film from
      benzene solution

GAMESCO G

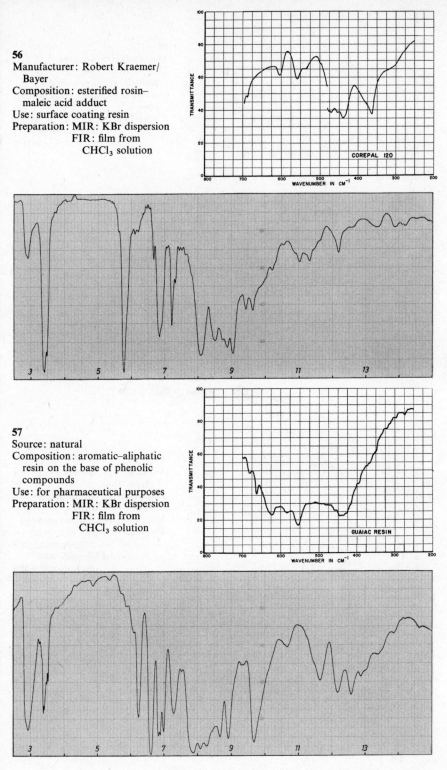

56
Manufacturer: Robert Kraemer/
 Bayer
Composition: esterified rosin–
 maleic acid adduct
Use: surface coating resin
Preparation: MIR: KBr dispersion
    FIR: film from
      CHCl₃ solution

COREPAL 120

57
Source: natural
Composition: aromatic–aliphatic
 resin on the base of phenolic
 compounds
Use: for pharmaceutical purposes
Preparation: MIR: KBr dispersion
    FIR: film from
      CHCl₃ solution

GUAIAC RESIN

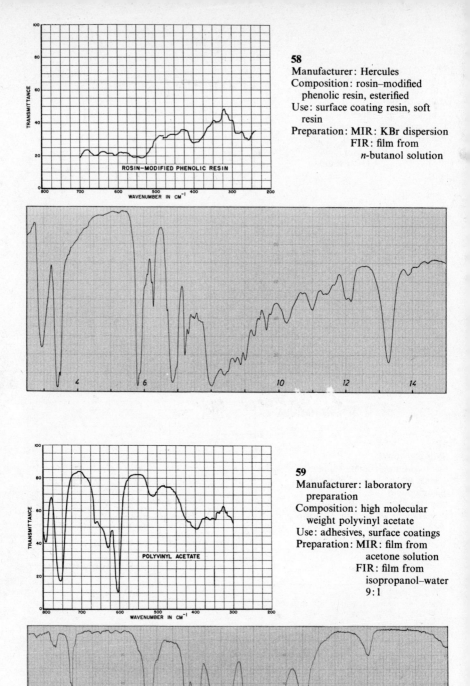

58

Manufacturer: Hercules
Composition: rosin–modified
  phenolic resin, esterified
Use: surface coating resin, soft
  resin
Preparation: MIR: KBr dispersion
         FIR: film from
           n-butanol solution

ROSIN–MODIFIED PHENOLIC RESIN

59

Manufacturer: laboratory
  preparation
Composition: high molecular
  weight polyvinyl acetate
Use: adhesives, surface coatings
Preparation: MIR: film from
         acetone solution
       FIR: film from
         isopropanol–water
         9:1

POLYVINYL ACETATE

PVAc (MG~10⁶)

120

60

Manufacturer: Goodrich
Composition: polyacrylic acid
Use: for thickeners
Preparation: MIR: film
         FIR: KBr dispersion

61

Manufacturer: BASF
Composition: sodium salt of
    polyacrylic acid
Use: for thickeners
Preparation: film of aqueous
    solution

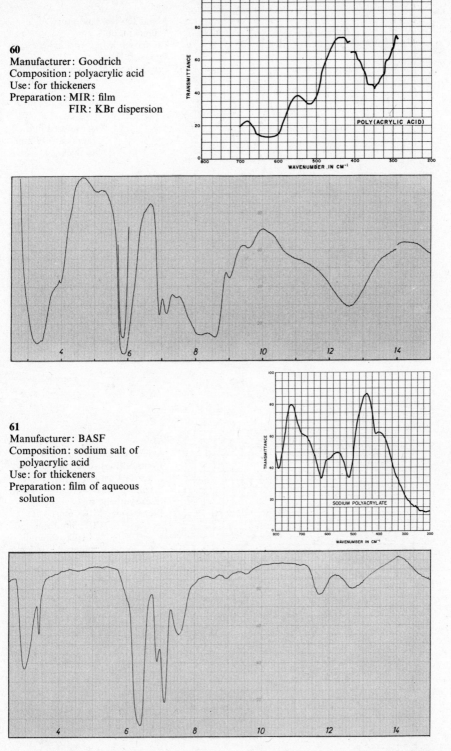

POLY(ACRYLIC ACID)

SODIUM POLYACRYLATE

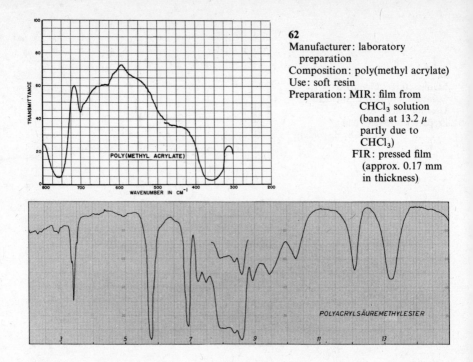

62

Manufacturer: laboratory preparation
Composition: poly(methyl acrylate)
Use: soft resin
Preparation: MIR: film from CHCl₃ solution (band at 13.2 μ partly due to CHCl₃)
FIR: pressed film (approx. 0.17 mm in thickness)

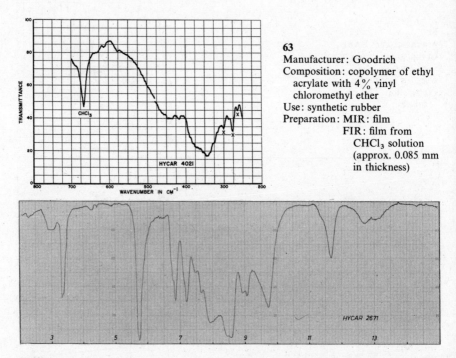

63

Manufacturer: Goodrich
Composition: copolymer of ethyl acrylate with 4% vinyl chloromethyl ether
Use: synthetic rubber
Preparation: MIR: film
FIR: film from CHCl₃ solution (approx. 0.085 mm in thickness)

64

Manufacturer: BASF
Composition: polybutyl acrylate
Use: for surface coatings
Preparation: film

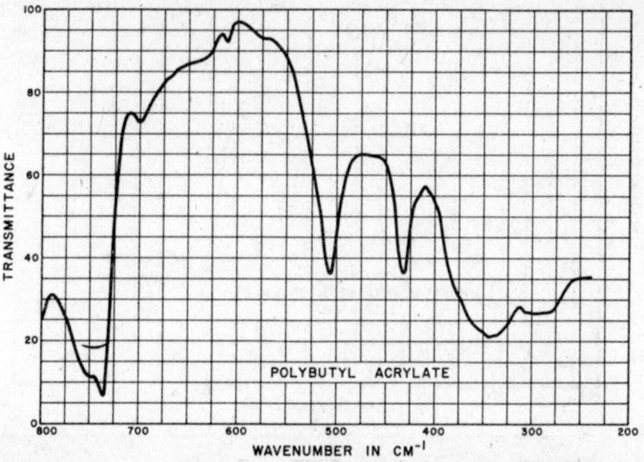

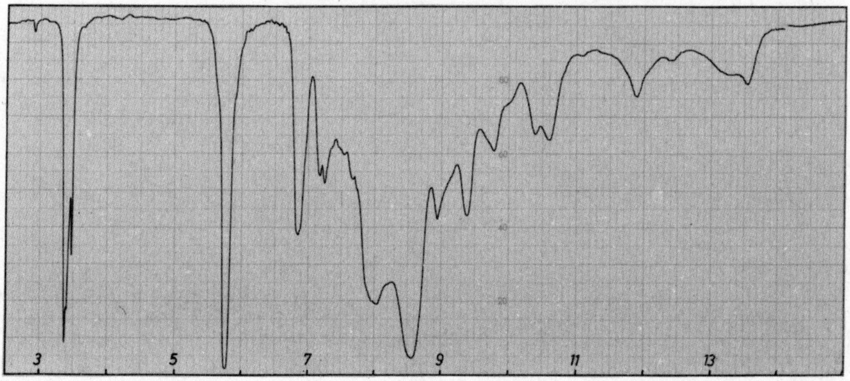

POLYBUTYL ACRYLATE

65

Manufacturer: laboratory
   preparation
Composition: polymethyacrylic
   acid (band at 665 cm^{-1} is due to
   atmospheric absorption)
Preparation: MIR: KBr dispersion
             FIR: film from
                  dioxane solution

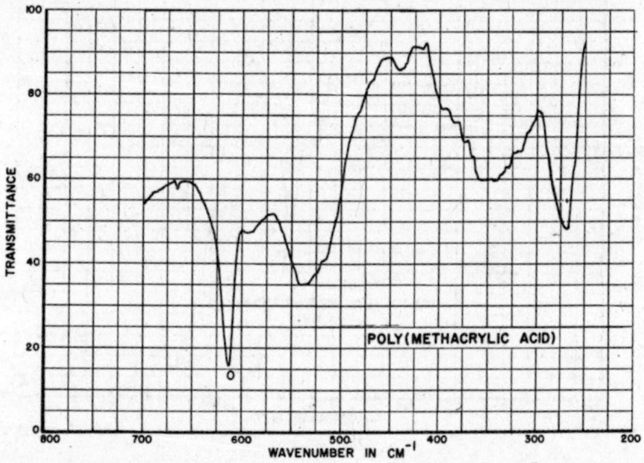

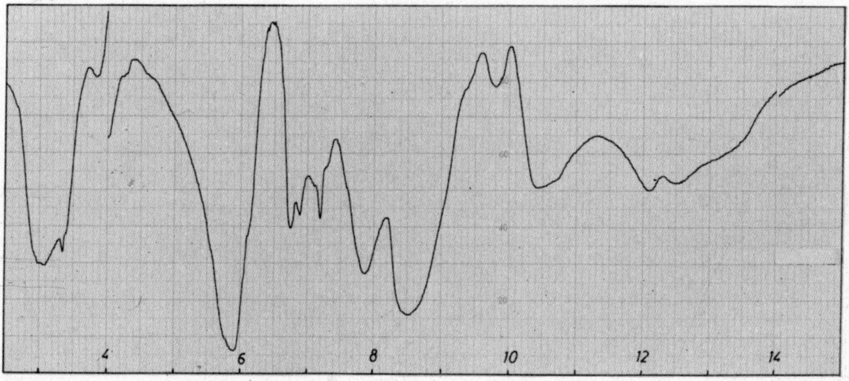

POLY(METHACRYLIC ACID)

123

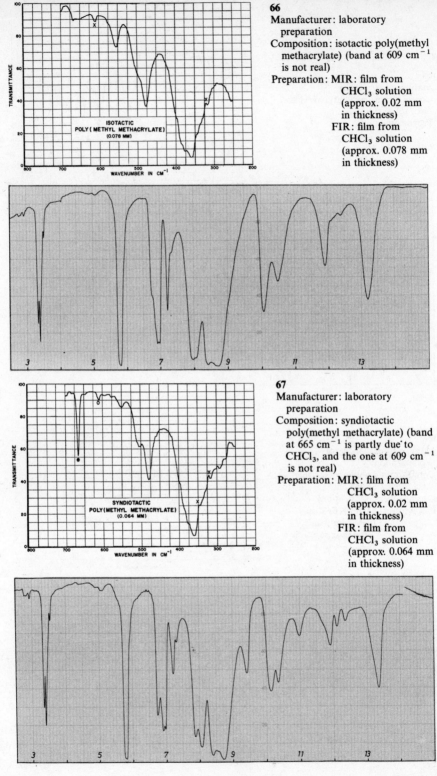

66

Manufacturer: laboratory preparation

Composition: isotactic poly(methyl methacrylate) (band at 609 cm^{-1} is not real)

Preparation: MIR: film from CHCl$_3$ solution (approx. 0.02 mm in thickness)
FIR: film from CHCl$_3$ solution (approx. 0.078 mm in thickness)

67

Manufacturer: laboratory preparation

Composition: syndiotactic poly(methyl methacrylate) (band at 665 cm^{-1} is partly due to CHCl$_3$, and the one at 609 cm^{-1} is not real)

Preparation: MIR: film from CHCl$_3$ solution (approx. 0.02 mm in thickness)
FIR: film from CHCl$_3$ solution (approx. 0.064 mm in thickness)

ISOTACTIC POLY (METHYL METHACRYLATE) (0.078 MM)

SYNDIOTACTIC POLY(METHYL METHACRYLATE) (0.064 MM)

124

68

Manufacturer: Röhm & Haas
Composition: atactic poly(methyl
  methacrylate) (band at 665 cm^{-1}
  is partly due to CHCl$_3$)
Preparation: MIR: film from ethyl
  acetate solution
  (approx. 0.016 mm
  in thickness)
  FIR: film from
  CHCl$_3$ solution

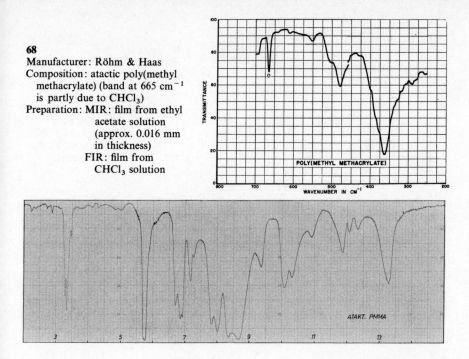

69

Manufacturer: laboratory
  preparation
Composition: poly(ethyl
  methacrylate)
Preparation: MIR: film from
  acetone solution
  (approx. 0.035 mm
  in thickness)
  FIR: film from
  CHCl$_3$ solution
  (approx. 0.36 mm
  in thickness)

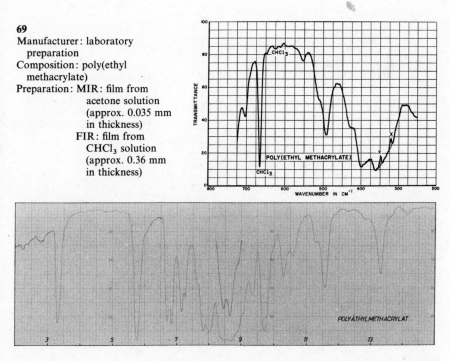

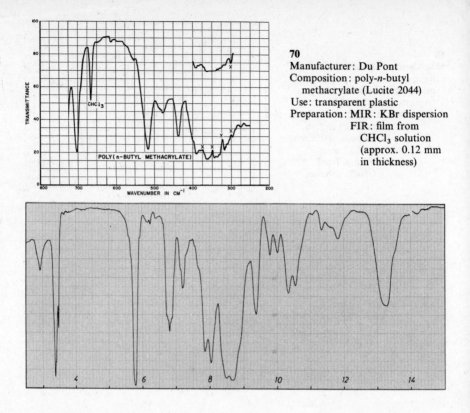

70
Manufacturer: Du Pont
Composition: poly-*n*-butyl
   methacrylate (Lucite 2044)
Use: transparent plastic
Preparation: MIR: KBr dispersion
      FIR: film from
        CHCl₃ solution
        (approx. 0.12 mm
        in thickness)

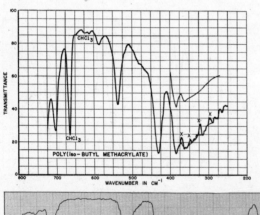

71
Manufacturer: Du Pont
Composition: poly(isobutyl
   methacrylate) (Lucite 2045)
Use: transparent plastic
Preparation: film from CHCl₃
   solution

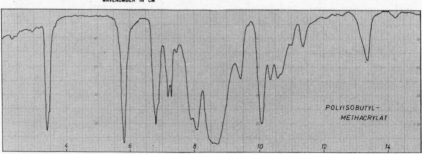

72

Manufacturer: Kalle
Composition: regenerated cellulose
Use: films
Preparation: MIR: film (approx.
　　　　　　0.025 mm) and
　　　　　　KBr dispersion
　　　　　FIR: film (approx.
　　　　　　0.03 mm in
　　　　　　thickness)

73

Manufacturers: Fisher Science; Dow
Composition: methyl cellulose
Use: thickener for latices
Preparation: MIR: KBr dispersion
　　　　　　FIR: film from water
　　　　　　solution (approx.
　　　　　　0.03 mm in
　　　　　　thickness)

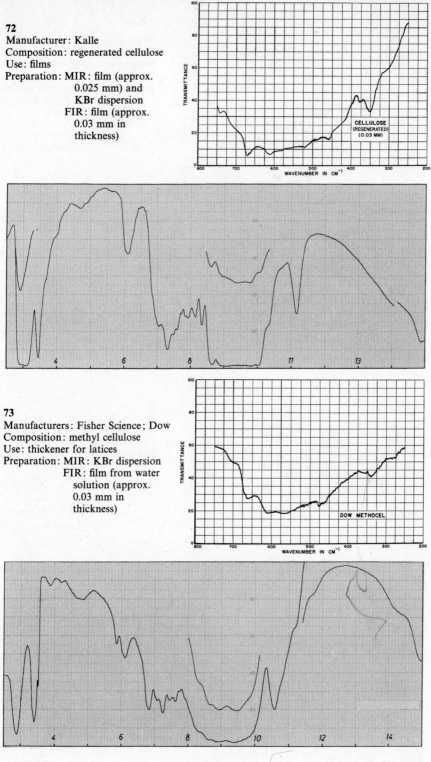

CELLULOSE
(REGENERATED)
(0.03 MM)

DOW METHOCEL

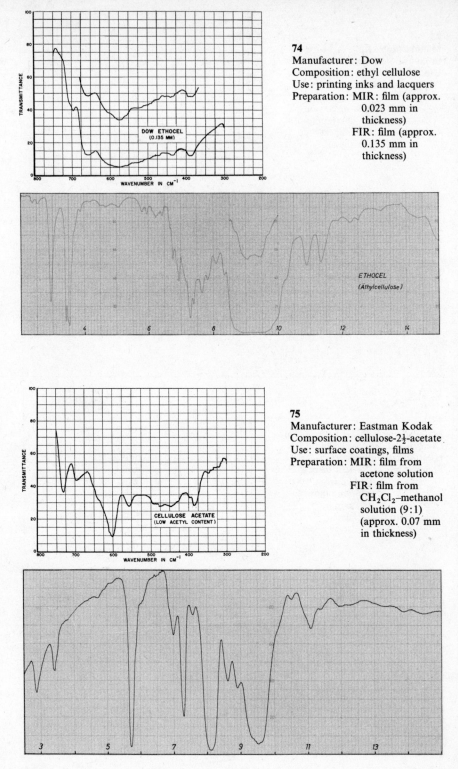

74
Manufacturer: Dow
Composition: ethyl cellulose
Use: printing inks and lacquers
Preparation: MIR: film (approx.
0.023 mm in
thickness)
FIR: film (approx.
0.135 mm in
thickness)

DOW ETHOCEL
(0.135 MM)

ETHOCEL
(Äthylcellulose)

75
Manufacturer: Eastman Kodak
Composition: cellulose-2½-acetate
Use: surface coatings, films
Preparation: MIR: film from
acetone solution
FIR: film from
CH_2Cl_2–methanol
solution (9:1)
(approx. 0.07 mm
in thickness)

CELLULOSE ACETATE
(LOW ACETYL CONTENT)

76

Manufacturer: Eastman Kodak
Composition: cellulose triacetate,
  plasticized with a phosphate
  plasticizer (probably cresyl-
  diphenyl phosphate)
Use: surface coatings, films
Preparation: MIR: film (approx.
        0.03 mm) and KBr
        dispersion
      FIR: film (approx.
        0.03 mm)

77

Manufacturer: Eastman Kodak
Composition: cellulose acetate–
  butyrate, plasticized with a
  phthalate plasticizer
Use: films, surface coatings
Preparation: MIR: film (approx.
        0.025 mm) and
        KBr dispersion
      FIR: film

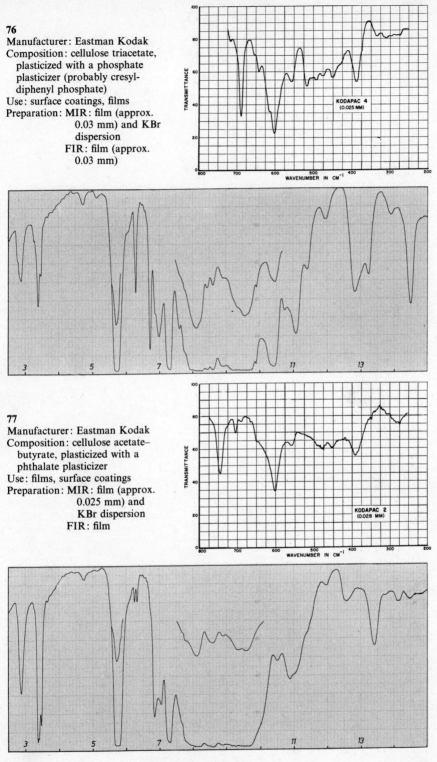

129

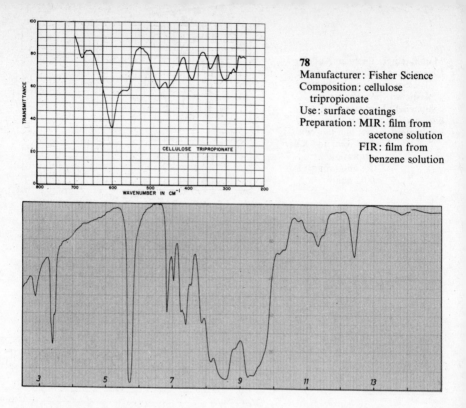

78
Manufacturer: Fisher Science
Composition: cellulose
    tripropionate
Use: surface coatings
Preparation: MIR: film from
        acetone solution
      FIR: film from
        benzene solution

CELLULOSE TRIPROPIONATE

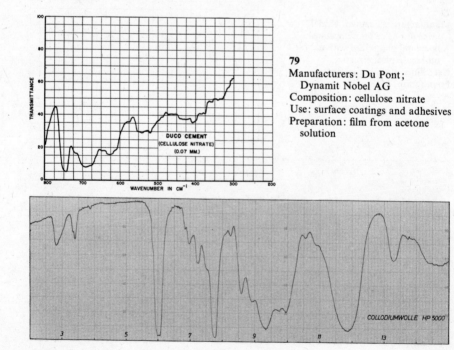

79
Manufacturers: Du Pont;
    Dynamit Nobel AG
Composition: cellulose nitrate
Use: surface coatings and adhesives
Preparation: film from acetone
    solution

DUCO CEMENT
(CELLULOSE NITRATE)
(0.07 MM.)

COLLODIUMWOLLE HP 5000

80

Manufacturer: Du Pont
Composition: polyoxymethylene
Use: for plastics of all kinds
Preparation: KBr dispersions

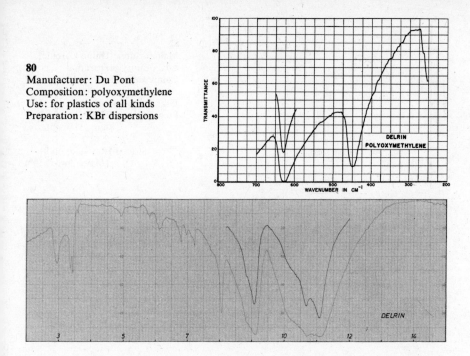

DELRIN
POLYOXYMETHYLENE

DELRIN

81

Manufacturer: Union Carbide
Composition: polyoxyethylene
glycol
Use: for textile and pharmaceutical
purposes
Preparation: liquid film

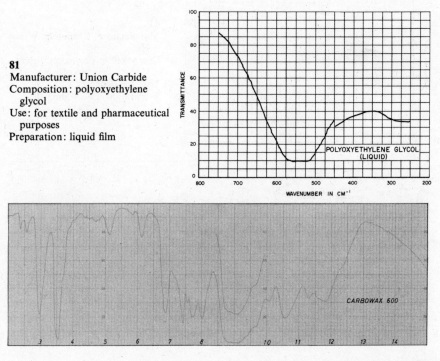

POLYOXYETHYLENE GLYCOL
(LIQUID)

CARBOWAX 600

131

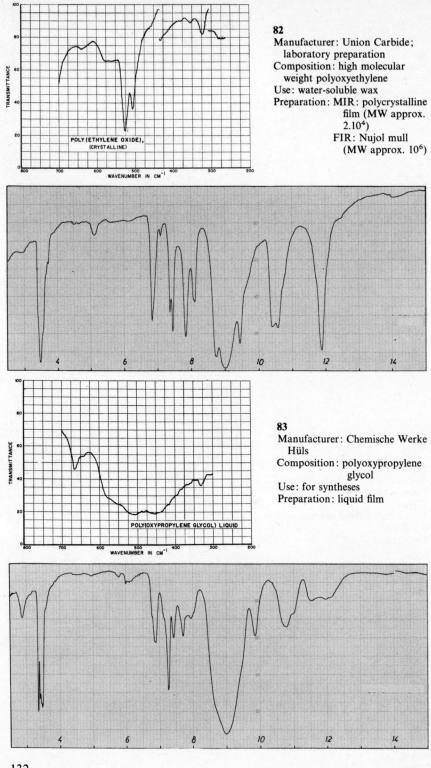

82

Manufacturer: Union Carbide;
    laboratory preparation
Composition: high molecular
    weight polyoxyethylene
Use: water-soluble wax
Preparation: MIR: polycrystalline
         film (MW approx.
         2.10^4)
       FIR: Nujol mull
         (MW approx. 10^6)

POLY(ETHYLENE OXIDE),
(CRYSTALLINE)

83

Manufacturer: Chemische Werke
    Hüls
Composition: polyoxypropylene
          glycol
Use: for syntheses
Preparation: liquid film

POLY(OXYPROPYLENE GLYCOL) LIQUID

132

84

Manufacturer: BASF
Composition: acetaldehyde resin
Use: surface coating resin (obsolete)
Preparation: MIR: KBr dispersion
           FIR: film from
                $CHCl_3$ solution

85

Manufacturer: Chemische Werke
    Hüls
Composition: acetophenone–
    formaldehyde resin
Use: surface coating resin
Preparation: MIR: KBr dispersion
            FIR: film from
                $CHCl_3$ solution

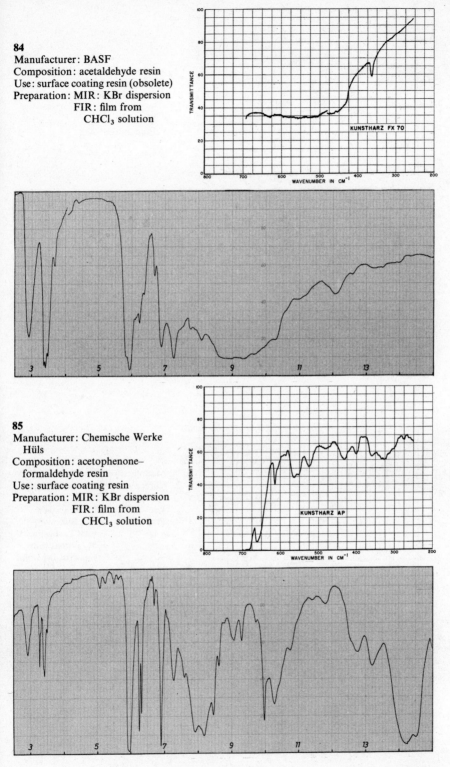

133

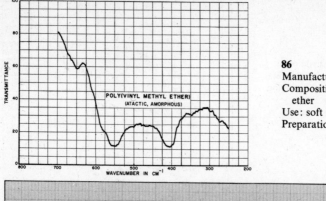

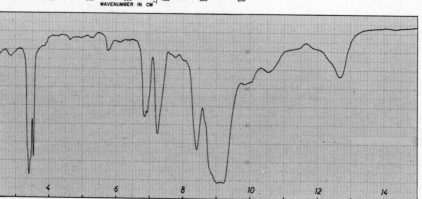

86
Manufacturer: BASF
Composition: polyvinyl methyl ether
Use: soft resin
Preparation: film

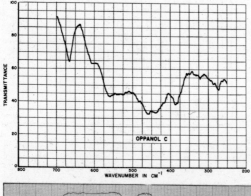

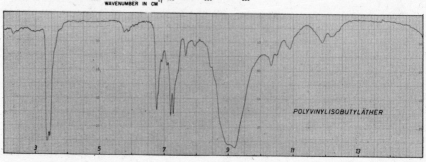

87
Manufacturer: BASF
Composition: polyvinyl isobutyl ether
Use: soft resin for adhesives
Preparation: MIR: film from CHCl$_3$ solution
FIR: pressed film (approx. 0.13 mm)

88

Manufacturer: Farbwerke Hoechst
Composition: polyvinyl formal
Use: for wire enamels
Preparation: MIR: KBr dispersion
FIR: film from
CHCl₃ solution

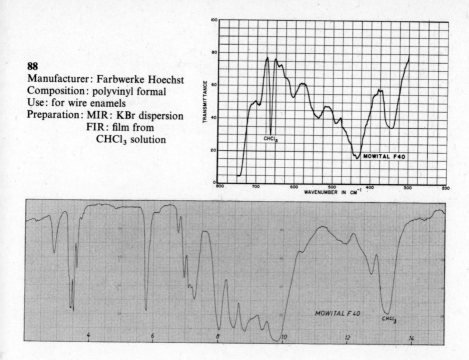

89

Manufacturer: Farbwerke Hoechst
Composition: polyvinyl butyral
Use: for wash primers and printing
inks
Preparation: MIR: film from
CHCl₃ solution
FIR: film from
CHCl₃ solution
(approx. 0.07 mm
in thickness)

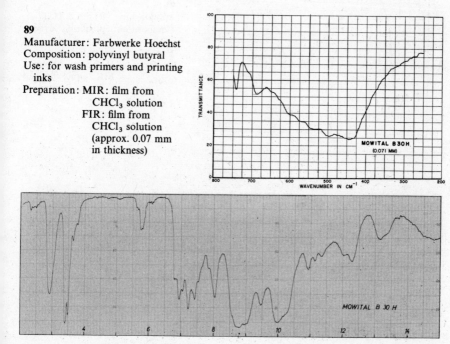

135

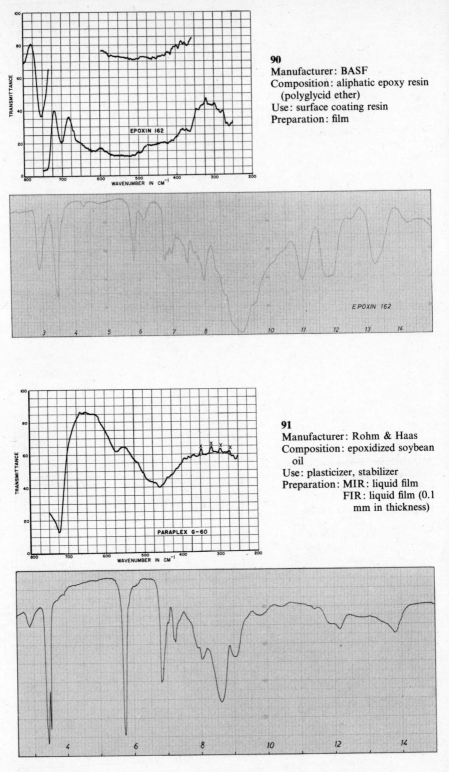

90
Manufacturer: BASF
Composition: aliphatic epoxy resin
 (polyglycid ether)
Use: surface coating resin
Preparation: film

EPOXIN 162

EPOXIN 162

91
Manufacturer: Rohm & Haas
Composition: epoxidized soybean
 oil
Use: plasticizer, stabilizer
Preparation: MIR: liquid film
 FIR: liquid film (0.1
 mm in thickness)

PARAPLEX G-60

92

Manufacturer: Shell
Composition: low molecular weight
 epoxy resin on base of 4,4′-
 dihydroxydiphenylpropane
 ("bisphenol A")
Use: curing masses
Preparation: film

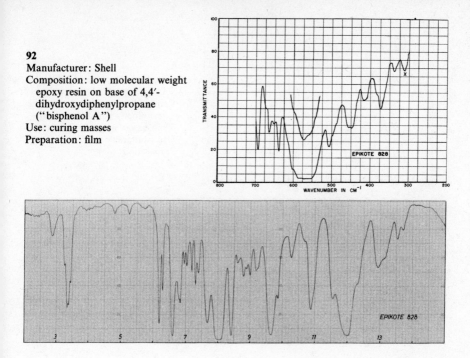

93

Manufacturer: Shell
Composition: high molecular
 weight epoxy resin on base of
 "bisphenol A"
Use: surface coating resin
Preparation: MIR: film from
 acetone solution
 FIR: film from
 CHCl₃ solution

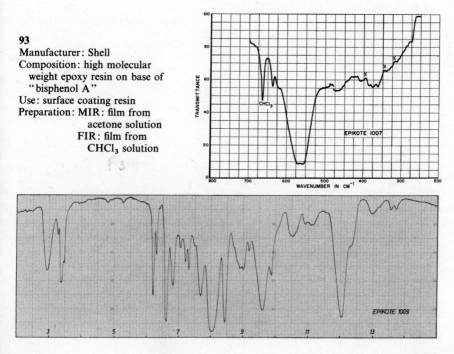

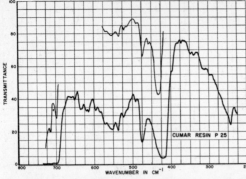

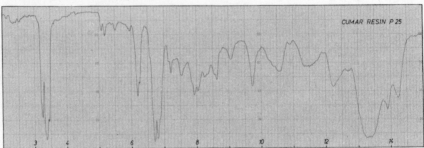

CUMAR RESIN P 25

94

Manufacturer: Allied Chemical
Dye Corp.
Composition: indene–coumarone
resin (main component: low
molecular weight polyindene)
Use: soft resin
Preparation: film

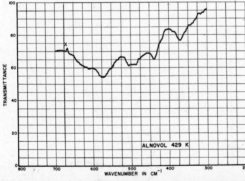

95

Manufacturer: Chemische Werke
Albert
Composition: cresol novolac
Use: for alcoholic lacquers
Preparation: MIR: KBr dispersion
FIR: film from
isopropanol solution

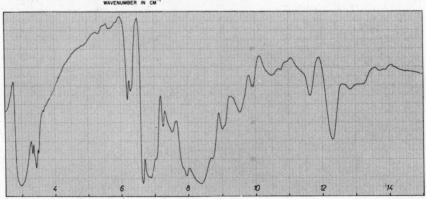

138

96

Manufacturer: Koppers
Composition: resorcinol–
    formaldehyde novolac
Preparation: MIR: film from ethyl
        acetate solution
        (1.5 mg cm^{-2})
    FIR: film from
        isopropanol solution

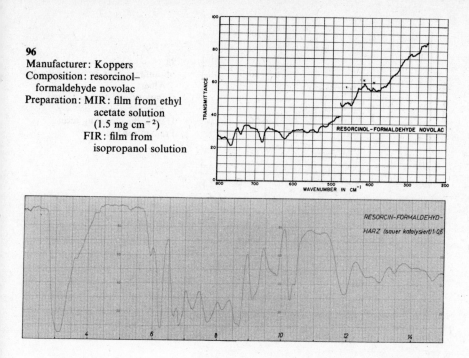

RESORCINOL–FORMALDEHYDE NOVOLAC

RESORCIN–FORMALDEHYD–
HARZ (sauer katalysiert) 1:0,6

97

Manufacturer: Chemische Werke
  Albert
Composition: curable phenol resole
Use: for epoxy combinations
Preparation: MIR: film from
        acetone solution
    FIR: KI dispersion

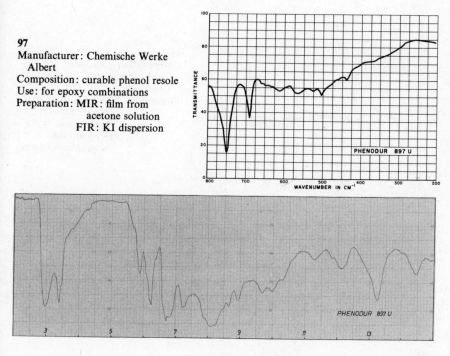

PHENODUR 897 U

PHENODUR 897 U

139

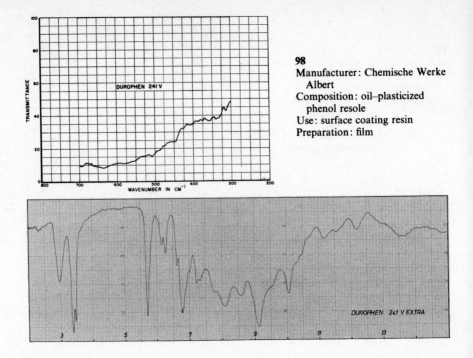

98
Manufacturer: Chemische Werke
    Albert
Composition: oil–plasticized
    phenol resole
Use: surface coating resin
Preparation: film

DUROPHEN 241 V

DUROPHEN 241 V EXTRA

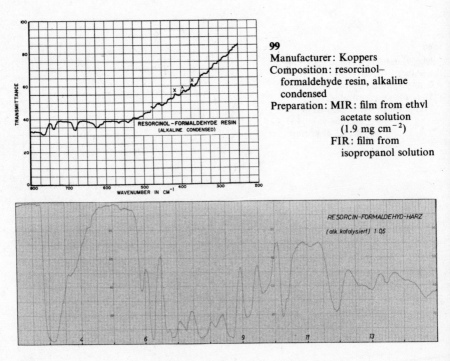

99
Manufacturer: Koppers
Composition: resorcinol–
    formaldehyde resin, alkaline
    condensed
Preparation: MIR: film from ethyl
    acetate solution
    (1.9 mg cm^{-2})
    FIR: film from
    isopropanol solution

RESORCINOL – FORMALDEHYDE RESIN
(ALKALINE CONDENSED)

RESORCIN–FORMALDEHYD–HARZ
(alk. katalysiert) 1:0.5

100

Manufacturer: Koppers
Composition: phenol–resorcinol
    formaldehyde resin (0.5:0.5:0.6,
    alkaline condensed)
Preparation: MIR: film from ethyl
          acetate (1.5 mg
          cm^{-2})
        FIR: film from
          isopropanol solution

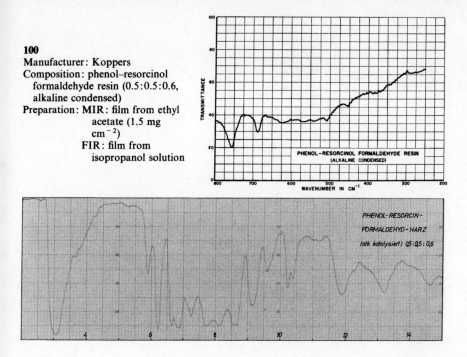

PHENOL–RESORCINOL FORMALDEHYDE RESIN
(ALKALINE CONDENSED)

PHENOL–RESORCIN–
FORMALDEHYD–HARZ
(alk. katalysiert) 0,5:0,5:0,6

101

Manufacturer: Bayer
Composition: polyamide-6,
    polycaprolactam
Use: plastics of all kinds
Preparation: films from formic acid
          solution (0.011,
          0.022, and 0.03 mm
          in thickness)

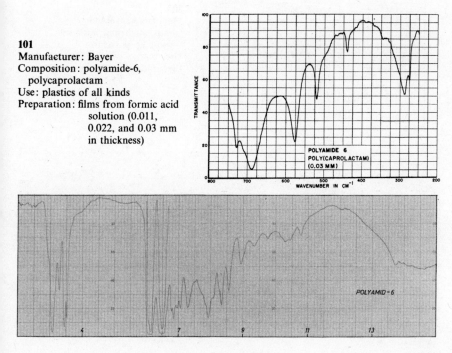

POLYAMIDE 6
POLY(CAPROLACTAM)
(0.03 MM)

POLYAMID–6

141

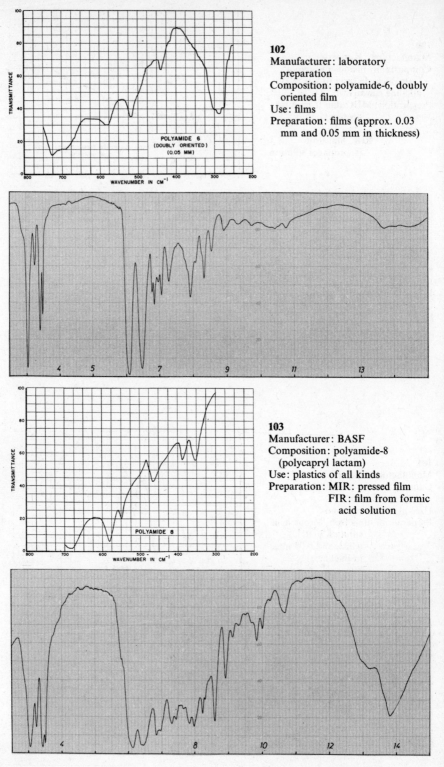

**POLYAMIDE 6
(DOUBLY ORIENTED)
(0.05 MM)**

102
Manufacturer: laboratory
  preparation
Composition: polyamide-6, doubly
  oriented film
Use: films
Preparation: films (approx. 0.03
  mm and 0.05 mm in thickness)

POLYAMIDE 8

103
Manufacturer: BASF
Composition: polyamide-8
  (polycapryl lactam)
Use: plastics of all kinds
Preparation: MIR: pressed film
  FIR: film from formic
  acid solution

104

Manufacturer: Organico
Composition: polyamide-11,
  polyundecyl lactam
Use: plastics of all kinds
Preparation: MIR: pressed film
        FIR: film from formic
        acid solution

105

Manufacturer: BASF
Composition: polyamide-6,6
Use: plastics of all kinds
Preparation: film from formic acid
  solution

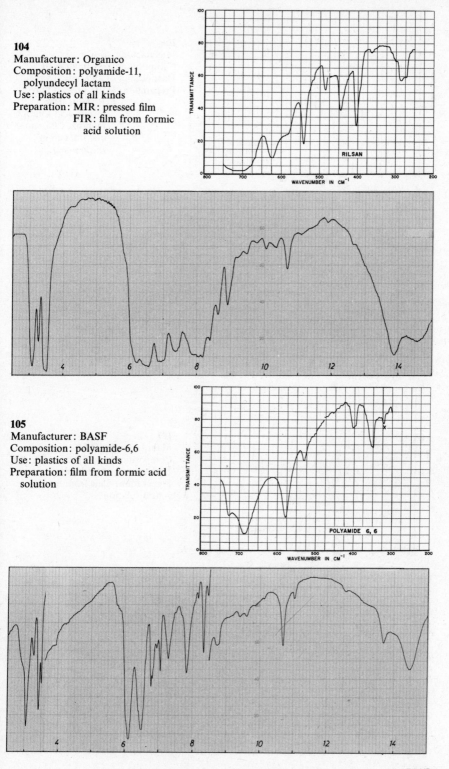

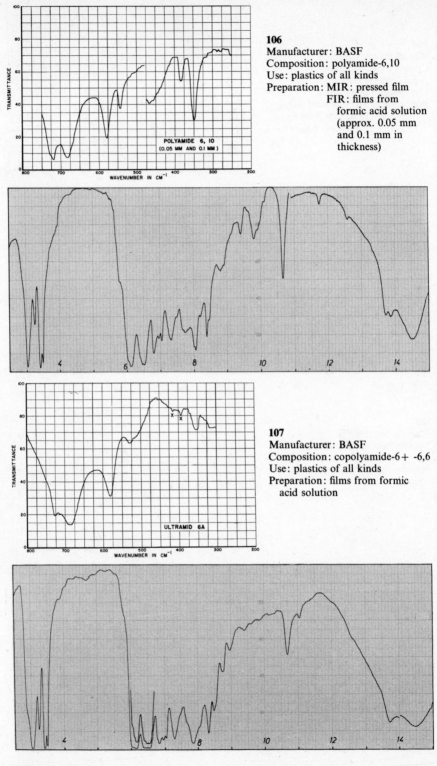

106
Manufacturer: BASF
Composition: polyamide-6,10
Use: plastics of all kinds
Preparation: MIR: pressed film
    FIR: films from
      formic acid solution
      (approx. 0.05 mm
      and 0.1 mm in
      thickness)

POLYAMIDE 6, 10
(0.05 MM AND 0.1 MM)

107
Manufacturer: BASF
Composition: copolyamide-6 + -6,6
Use: plastics of all kinds
Preparation: films from formic
  acid solution

ULTRAMID 6A

108

Manufacturer: BASF
Composition: terpolyamide-6 +
  -6,6 + diaminodicyclohexyl-
  methane adipate
Use: surface coating resin
Preparation: films from methanol–
  benzene solution 7:3

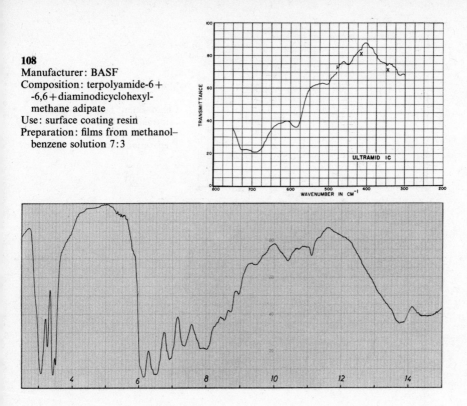

109

Manufacturer: General Mills
Composition: polyamide from di-
  and trimerized fatty acids and di-
  or polyamines
Use: for epoxy combinations
Preparation: film

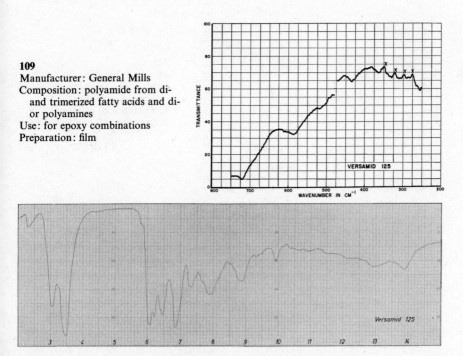

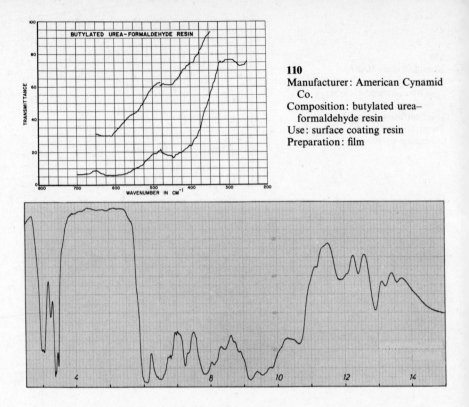

110

Manufacturer: American Cynamid
　　Co.
Composition: butylated urea–
　　formaldehyde resin
Use: surface coating resin
Preparation: film

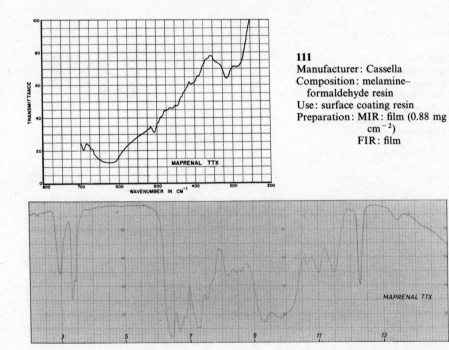

111

Manufacturer: Cassella
Composition: melamine–
　　formaldehyde resin
Use: surface coating resin
Preparation: MIR: film (0.88 mg
　　　　　　　　　cm^{-2})
　　　　　　　FIR: film

112

Manufacturer: CIBA

Composition: oil-modified melamine–formaldehyde resin

Use: surface coating resin

Preparation: MIR: film (0.8 mg
cm⁻²)
FIR: film

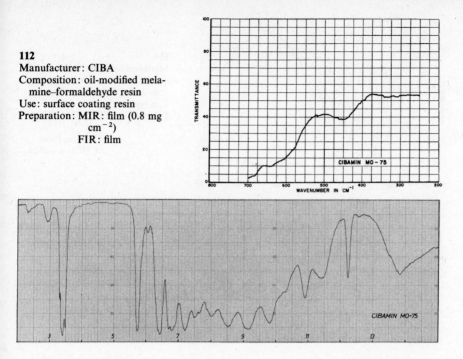

113

Manufacturer: Cassella

Composition: benzoguanamine–
formaldehyde resin

Use: surface coating resin

Preparation: film

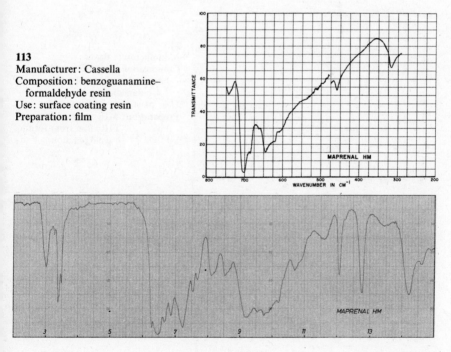

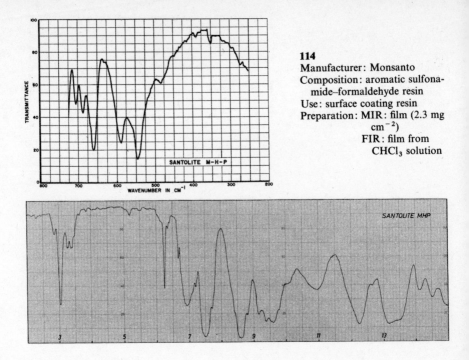

114
Manufacturer: Monsanto
Composition: aromatic sulfona-
    mide–formaldehyde resin
Use: surface coating resin
Preparation: MIR: film (2.3 mg
        cm^{-2})
       FIR: film from
         $CHCl_3$ solution

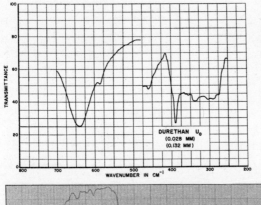

115
Manufacturer: Bayer
Composition: polyurethane from
    hexamethylene diisocyanate and
    1,4-butanediol
Use: plastics of all kinds
Preparation: MIR: pressed film
        FIR: film from formic
         acid solution

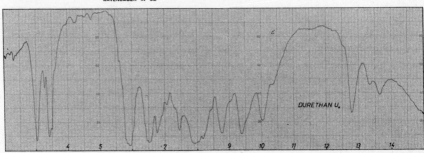

116

Manufacturer: Du Pont
Composition: polyether reacted
  with toluene diisocyanate
Use: synthetic urethane elastomer
Preparation: film

117

Manufacturer: Du Pont
Composition: polyether reacted
  with toluene diisocyanate
Use: synthetic urethane elastomer
Preparation: film

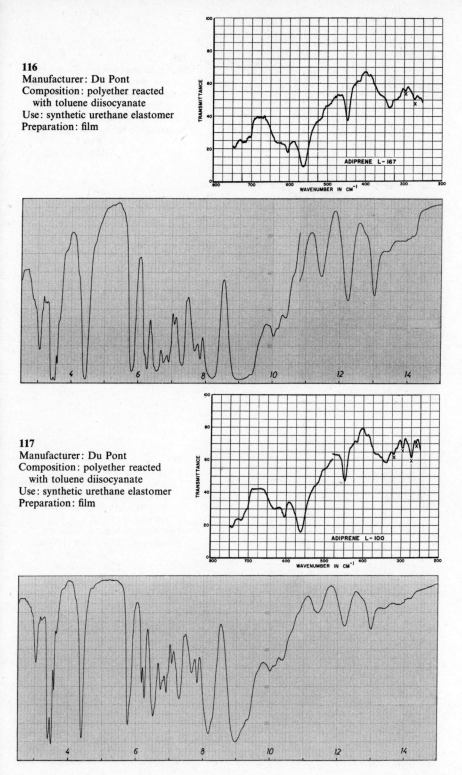

ADIPRENE L-167

ADIPRENE L-100

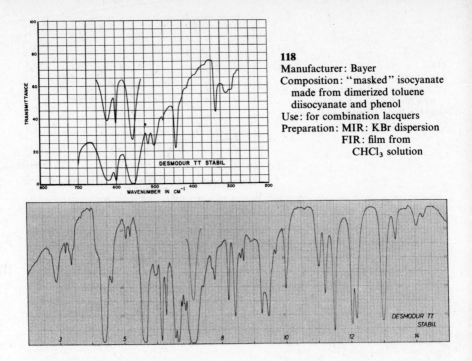

118
Manufacturer: Bayer
Composition: "masked" isocyanate
made from dimerized toluene
diisocyanate and phenol
Use: for combination lacquers
Preparation: MIR: KBr dispersion
FIR: film from
CHCl₃ solution

DESMODUR TT STABIL

DESMODUR TT
STABIL

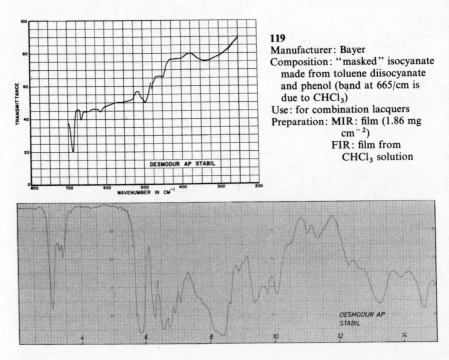

119
Manufacturer: Bayer
Composition: "masked" isocyanate
made from toluene diisocyanate
and phenol (band at 665/cm is
due to CHCl₃)
Use: for combination lacquers
Preparation: MIR: film (1.86 mg
cm⁻²)
FIR: film from
CHCl₃ solution

DESMODUR AP STABIL

DESMODUR AP
STABIL

150

120

Manufacturer: Du Pont
Composition: 4,4′-methylenedi-*o*-
  tolyl isocyanate
Use: for combination lacquers
Preparation: film

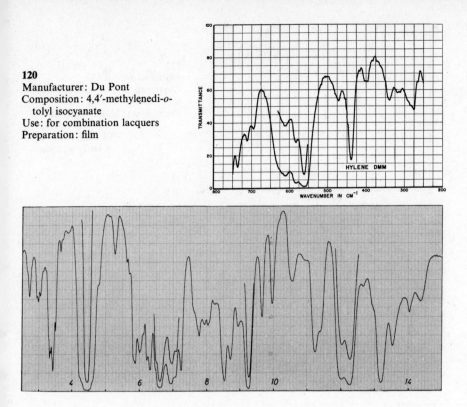

121

Manufacturer: laboratory
  preparation
Composition: copolymer of
  acrylonitrile with 6% vinyl
  acetate
Preparation: MIR: KBr dispersion
        FIR: Nujol mull

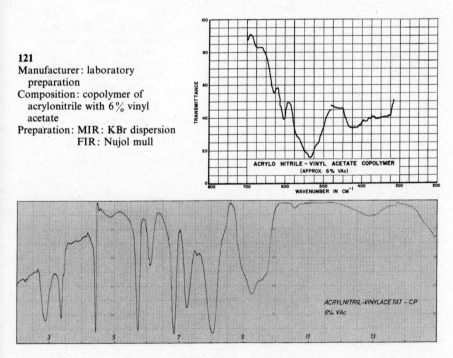

151

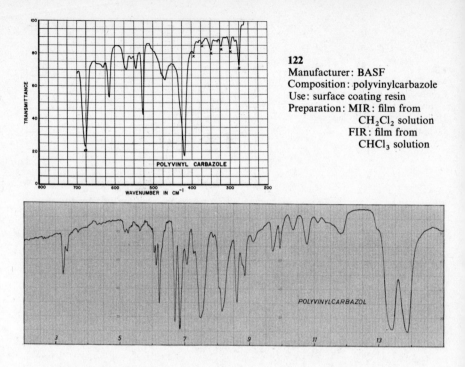

122
Manufacturer: BASF
Composition: polyvinylcarbazole
Use: surface coating resin
Preparation: MIR: film from
　　　　　CH_2Cl_2 solution
　　　　FIR: film from
　　　　　$CHCl_3$ solution

POLYVINYL CARBAZOLE

POLYVINYLCARBAZOL

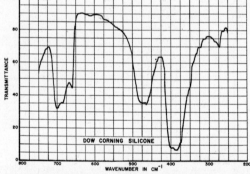

123
Manufacturers: Dow; Bayer
Composition: poly(dimethyl-
　　siloxane)
Use: grease
Preparation: film (approx. 0.005
　mm in thickness)

DOW CORNING SILICONE

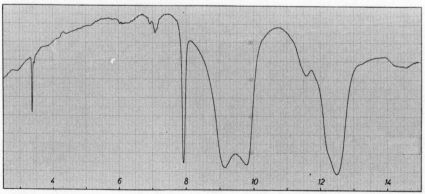

124

Manufacturer: Dow
Composition: poly(methylphenyl-
siloxane)
Preparation: film

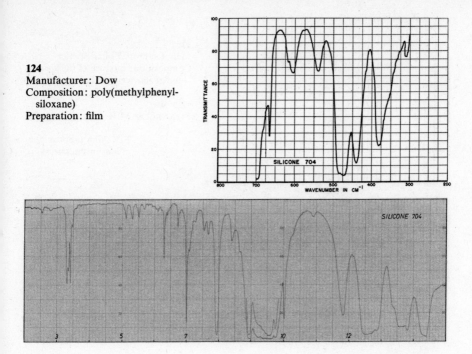

125

Manufacturer: Esso
Composition: bituminous aliphatic
hydrocarbons
Use: surface coatings
Preparation: MIR: film from
CHCl₃
FIR: film

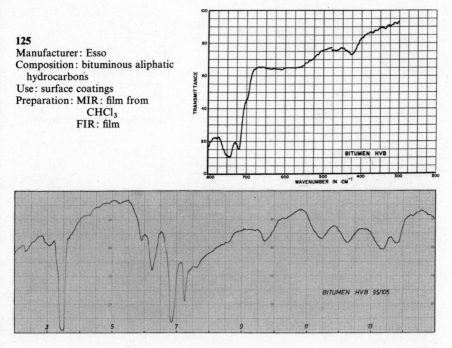

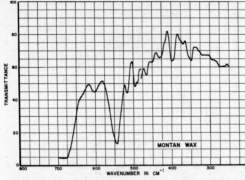

126

Manufacturer: Fisher Science
Composition: mixture of high
   molecular weight aliphatic fatty
   acids and esters
Use: wax
Preparation: MIR: film (5.2 mg
           cm^{-2})
      FIR: film (approx. 0.6
        mm in thickness)

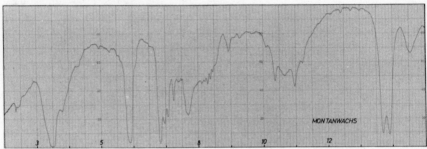

127

Source: natural
Composition: mixture of high
   molecular weight aliphatic esters
   and acids
Use: wax
Preparation: polycrystalline film

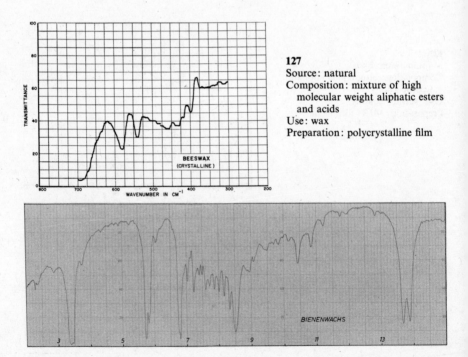

128

Source: natural

Composition: mixture of high
molecular weight aliphatic
hydrocarbons, alcohols, and
esters

Use: wax

Preparation: MIR: polycrystalline
film
FIR: polycrystalline
film (approx. 0.3
mm in thickness)

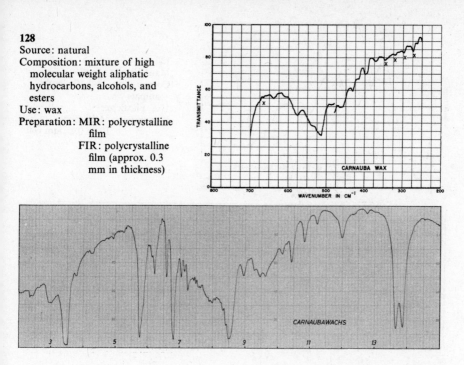

CARNAUBA WAX

CARNAUBAWACHS

129

Source: natural

Composition: mixture of high
molecular weight aliphatic
hydrocarbons, and ester-type
and acid resins

Use: wax

Preparation: MIR: polycrystalline
film
FIR: film (approx. 1.5
mm in thickness)

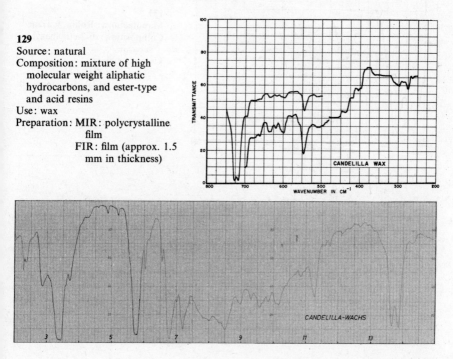

CANDELILLA WAX

CANDELILLA-WACHS

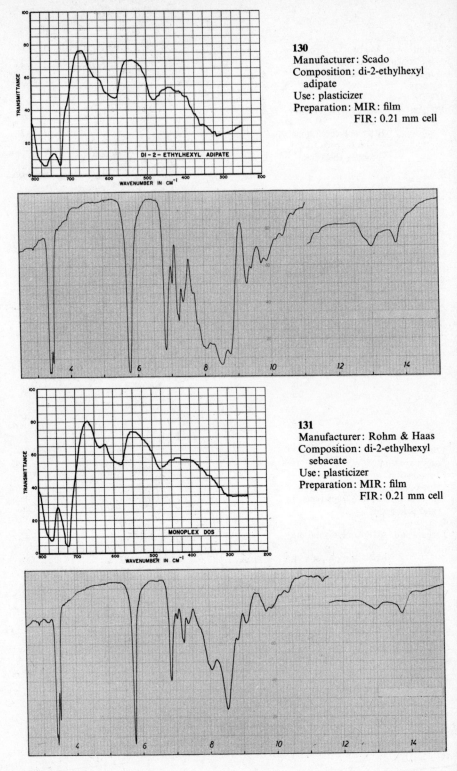

130
Manufacturer: Scado
Composition: di-2-ethylhexyl
adipate
Use: plasticizer
Preparation: MIR: film
FIR: 0.21 mm cell

DI - 2 - ETHYLHEXYL ADIPATE

131
Manufacturer: Rohm & Haas
Composition: di-2-ethylhexyl
sebacate
Use: plasticizer
Preparation: MIR: film
FIR: 0.21 mm cell

MONOPLEX DOS

132

Manufacturer: BASF
Composition: dimethyl phthalate
Use: plasticizer
Preparation: MIR: film
　　　　　FIR: 0.1 mm cell

133

Manufacturer: BASF
Composition: diethyl phthalate
Use: plasticizer
Preparation: MIR: film
　　　　　FIR: 0.1 mm cell

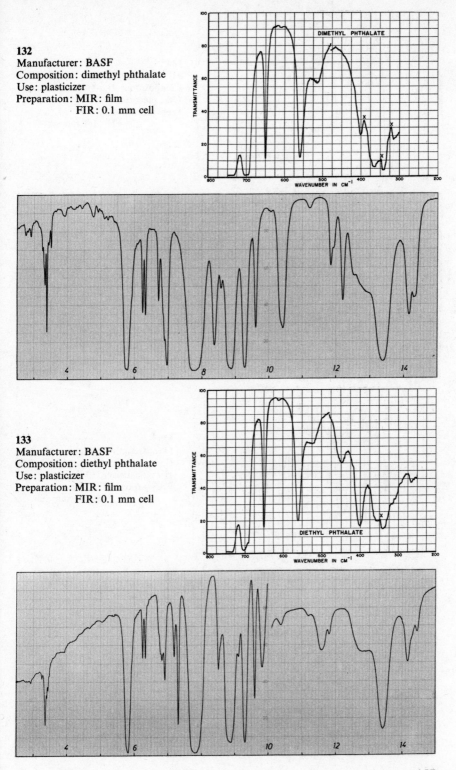

DIMETHYL PHTHALATE

DIETHYL PHTHALATE

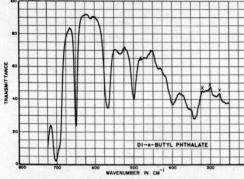

DI-n-BUTYL PHTHALATE

134
Manufacturer: BASF
Composition: di-*n*-butyl phthalate
Use: plasticizer
Preparation: MIR: film
FIR: 0.1 mm cell

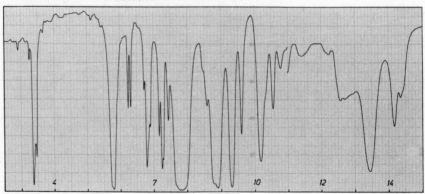

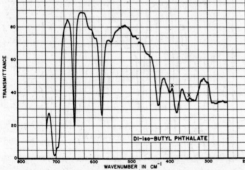

DI-iso-BUTYL PHTHALATE

135
Manufacturer: Eastman
Composition: diisobutyl phthalate
Use: plasticizer
Preparation: MIR: film
FIR: 0.1 mm cell

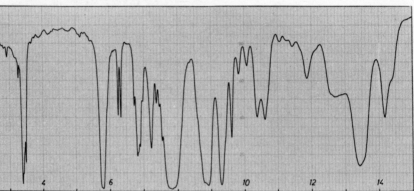

158

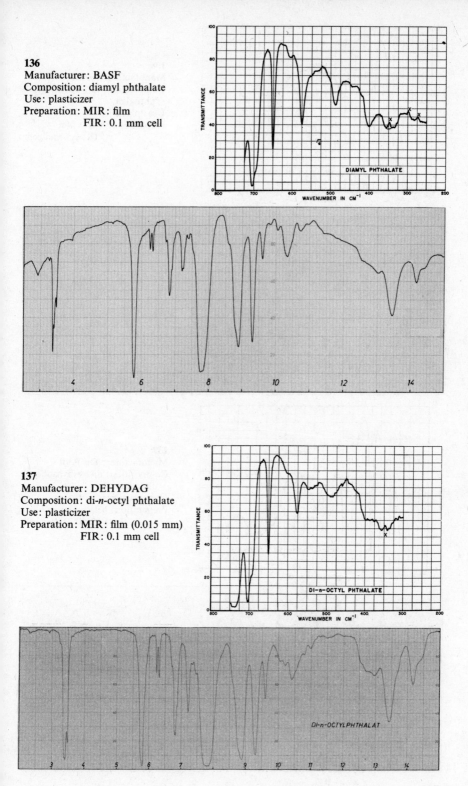

136
Manufacturer: BASF
Composition: diamyl phthalate
Use: plasticizer
Preparation: MIR: film
                FIR: 0.1 mm cell

DIAMYL PHTHALATE

137
Manufacturer: DEHYDAG
Composition: di-*n*-octyl phthalate
Use: plasticizer
Preparation: MIR: film (0.015 mm)
                FIR: 0.1 mm cell

DI-n-OCTYL PHTHALATE

DI-n-OCTYLPHTHALAT

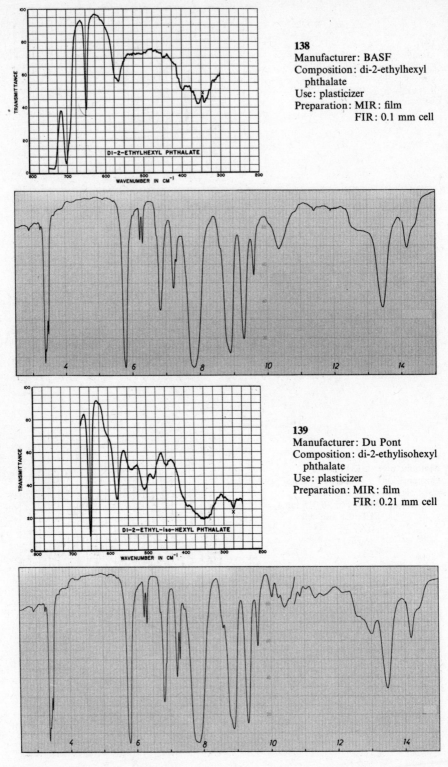

138
Manufacturer: BASF
Composition: di-2-ethylhexyl
   phthalate
Use: plasticizer
Preparation: MIR: film
          FIR: 0.1 mm cell

DI-2-ETHYLHEXYL PHTHALATE

TRANSMITTANCE

WAVENUMBER IN CM⁻¹

139
Manufacturer: Du Pont
Composition: di-2-ethylisohexyl
   phthalate
Use: plasticizer
Preparation: MIR: film
          FIR: 0.21 mm cell

DI-2-ETHYL-iso-HEXYL PHTHALATE

TRANSMITTANCE

WAVENUMBER IN CM⁻¹

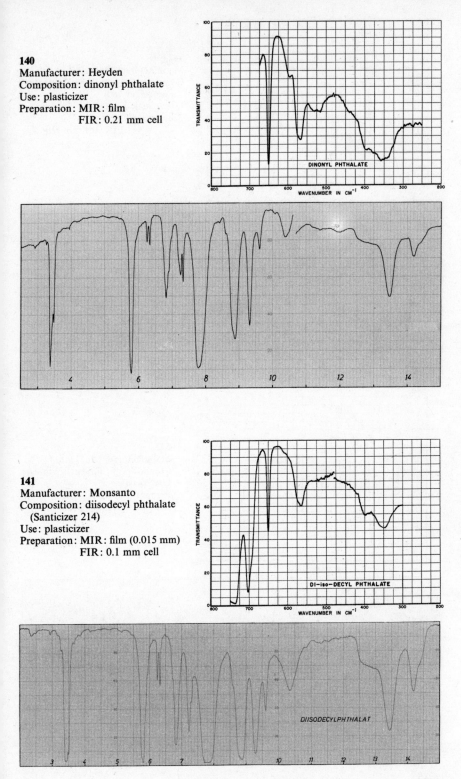

140
Manufacturer: Heyden
Composition: dinonyl phthalate
Use: plasticizer
Preparation: MIR: film
       FIR: 0.21 mm cell

DINONYL PHTHALATE

WAVENUMBER IN CM⁻¹

141
Manufacturer: Monsanto
Composition: diisodecyl phthalate
  (Santicizer 214)
Use: plasticizer
Preparation: MIR: film (0.015 mm)
       FIR: 0.1 mm cell

DI-iso-DECYL PHTHALATE

WAVENUMBER IN CM⁻¹

DIISODECYLPHTHALAT

161

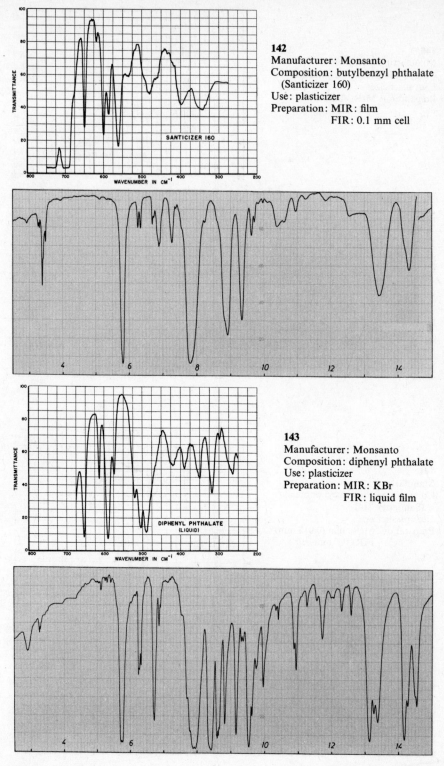

142
Manufacturer: Monsanto
Composition: butylbenzyl phthalate
(Santicizer 160)
Use: plasticizer
Preparation: MIR: film
FIR: 0.1 mm cell

SANTICIZER 160

143
Manufacturer: Monsanto
Composition: diphenyl phthalate
Use: plasticizer
Preparation: MIR: KBr
FIR: liquid film

DIPHENYL PHTHALATE
(LIQUID)

144
Manufacturer: BASF
Composition: dimethylglycol
  phthalate (Palatinol O)
Use: plasticizer
Preparation: MIR: liquid film
          FIR: 0.1 mm cell

145
Manufacturer: Monsanto
Composition: methylphthalylethyl
  glycolate (Santicizer M17)
Use: plasticizer
Preparation: MIR: liquid film
          (approx. 0.01 mm)
          FIR: 0.1 mm cell

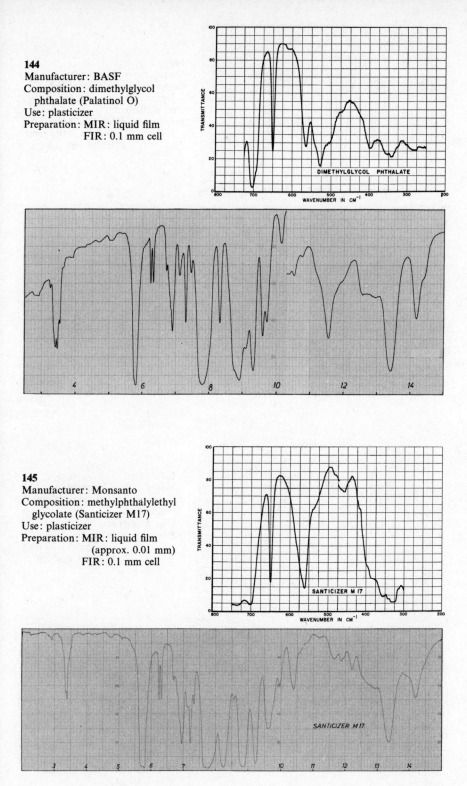

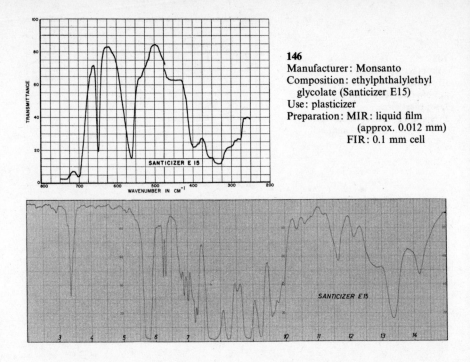

146
Manufacturer: Monsanto
Composition: ethylphthalylethyl
  glycolate (Santicizer E15)
Use: plasticizer
Preparation: MIR: liquid film
            (approx. 0.012 mm)
  FIR: 0.1 mm cell

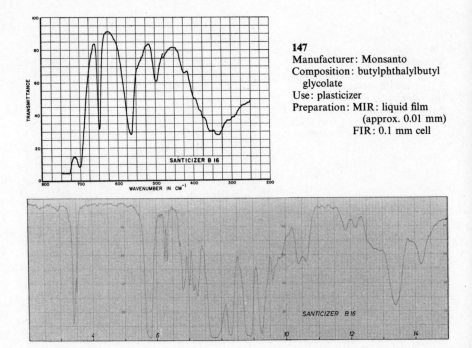

147
Manufacturer: Monsanto
Composition: butylphthalylbutyl
  glycolate
Use: plasticizer
Preparation: MIR: liquid film
            (approx. 0.01 mm)
  FIR: 0.1 mm cell

164

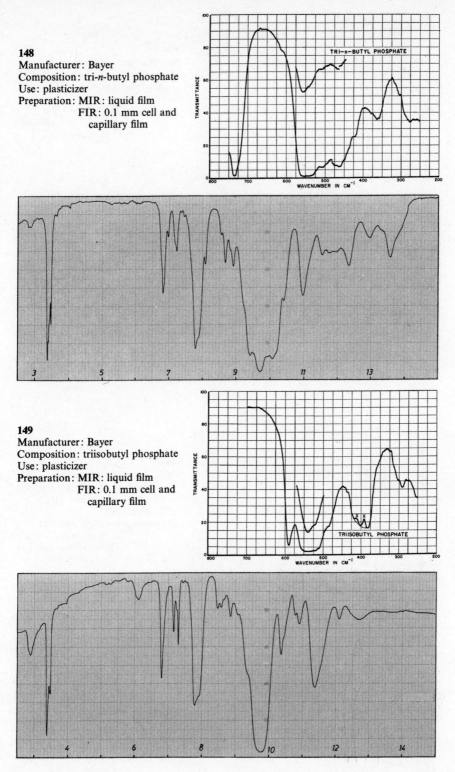

148
Manufacturer: Bayer
Composition: tri-*n*-butyl phosphate
Use: plasticizer
Preparation: MIR: liquid film
      FIR: 0.1 mm cell and
           capillary film

TRI-*n*-BUTYL PHOSPHATE

TRANSMITTANCE
WAVENUMBER IN CM⁻¹

149
Manufacturer: Bayer
Composition: triisobutyl phosphate
Use: plasticizer
Preparation: MIR: liquid film
      FIR: 0.1 mm cell and
           capillary film

TRIISOBUTYL PHOSPHATE

TRANSMITTANCE
WAVENUMBER IN CM⁻¹

165

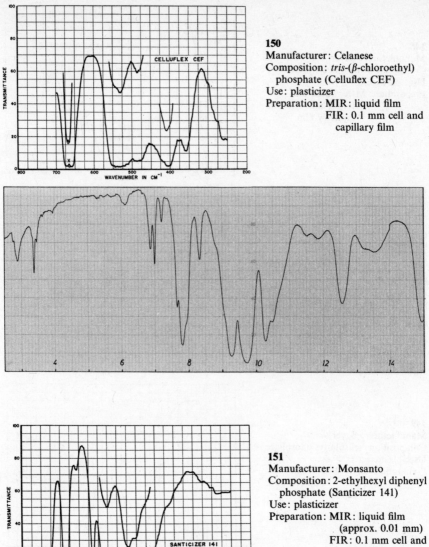

150
Manufacturer: Celanese
Composition: *tris*-(β-chloroethyl)
phosphate (Celluflex CEF)
Use: plasticizer
Preparation: MIR: liquid film
FIR: 0.1 mm cell and
capillary film

CELLUFLEX CEF

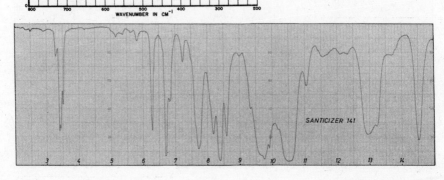

151
Manufacturer: Monsanto
Composition: 2-ethylhexyl diphenyl
phosphate (Santicizer 141)
Use: plasticizer
Preparation: MIR: liquid film
(approx. 0.01 mm)
FIR: 0.1 mm cell and
capillary film

SANTICIZER 141

152
Manufacturer: Monsanto
Composition: triphenyl phosphate
Use: plasticizer
Preparation: MIR: KBr dispersion
             FIR: liquid film

153
Manufacturer: Monsanto
Composition: cresyl diphenyl
  phosphate (Santicizer 140)
Use: plasticizer
Preparation: MIR: liquid film
          (approx. 0.015)
      FIR: 0.1 mm cell and
          capillary film

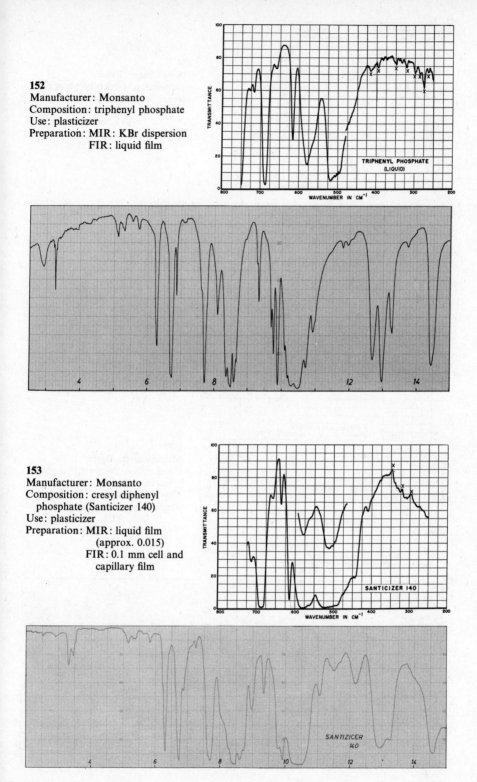

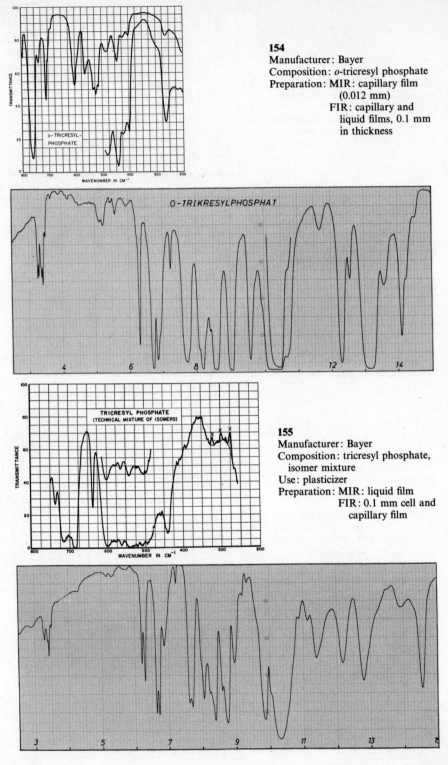

154

Manufacturer: Bayer
Composition: *o*-tricresyl phosphate
Preparation: MIR: capillary film
(0.012 mm)
FIR: capillary and
liquid films, 0.1 mm
in thickness

O-TRIKRESYLPHOSPHAT

TRICRESYL PHOSPHATE
(TECHNICAL MIXTURE OF ISOMERS)

155

Manufacturer: Bayer
Composition: tricresyl phosphate,
isomer mixture
Use: plasticizer
Preparation: MIR: liquid film
FIR: 0.1 mm cell and
capillary film

156

Manufacturer: Farbwerke Hoechst
Composition: trixylenyl phosphate
Use: plasticizer
Preparation: MIR: liquid film
　　　　　　FIR: 0.1 mm cell and
　　　　　　　　　 capillary film

157

Manufacturer: Monsanto
Composition: triphenyl phosphite
Use: plasticizer
Preparation: MIR: liquid film
　　　　　　The band at 10.5 μ is
　　　　　　due to an impurity
　　　　　　(aryl phosphate)
　　　　　　FIR: 0.1 mm cell

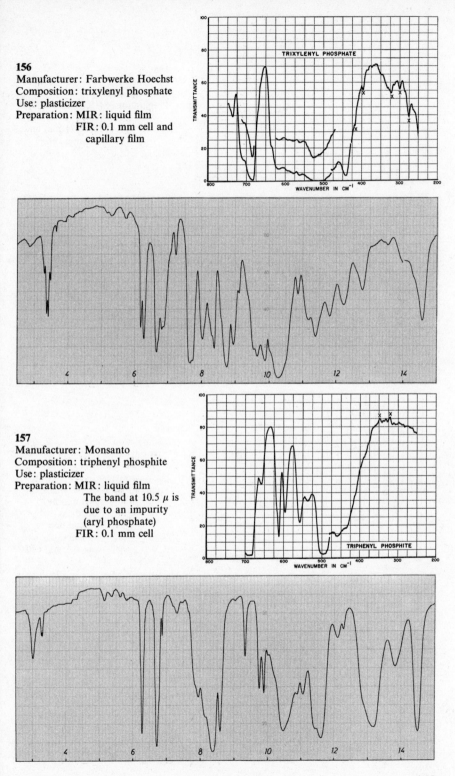

169

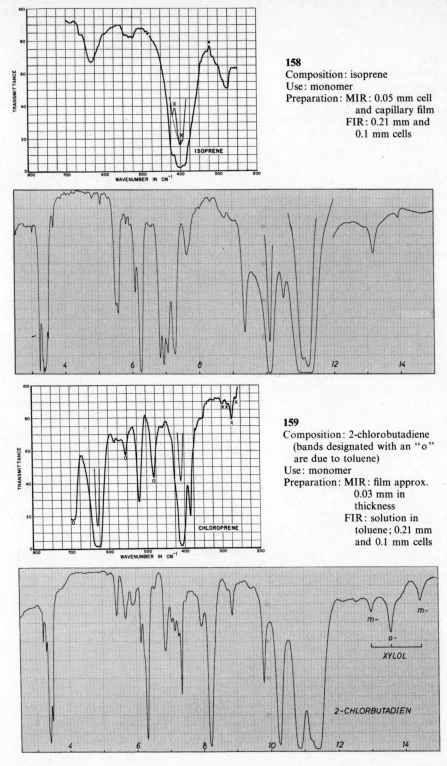

158
Composition: isoprene
Use: monomer
Preparation: MIR: 0.05 mm cell
and capillary film
FIR: 0.21 mm and
0.1 mm cells

ISOPRENE

159
Composition: 2-chlorobutadiene
(bands designated with an "o"
are due to toluene)
Use: monomer
Preparation: MIR: film approx.
0.03 mm in
thickness
FIR: solution in
toluene; 0.21 mm
and 0.1 mm cells

CHLOROPRENE

XYLOL

2-CHLORBUTADIEN

160
Composition: styrene
Use: monomer
Preparation: MIR: 0.02 mm cell
FIR: 0.09 mm cell

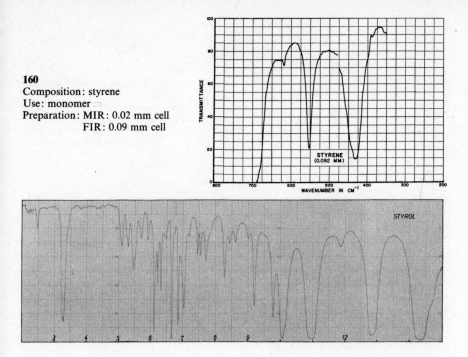

STYRENE
(0.092 MM)

STYROL

161
Composition: α-methylstyrene
Use: monomer
Preparation: MIR: 0.025 mm cell
FIR: 0.09 mm cell

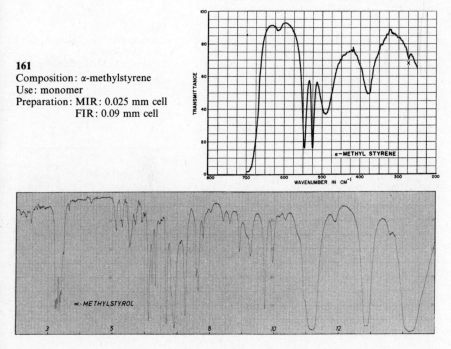

α-METHYL STYRENE

∝-METHYLSTYROL

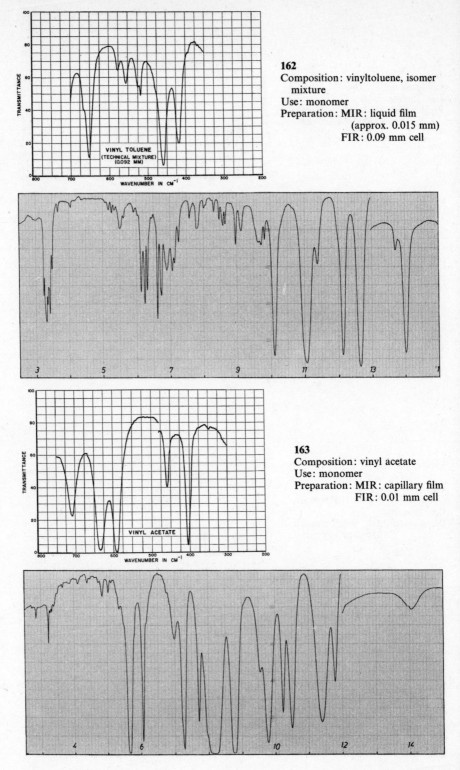

162
Composition: vinyltoluene, isomer
    mixture
Use: monomer
Preparation: MIR: liquid film
        (approx. 0.015 mm)
    FIR: 0.09 mm cell

VINYL TOLUENE
(TECHNICAL MIXTURE)
(0.092 MM)

163
Composition: vinyl acetate
Use: monomer
Preparation: MIR: capillary film
    FIR: 0.01 mm cell

VINYL ACETATE

164

Manufacturer: Matheson, Coleman
  and Bell
Composition: diallyl maleate
Use: monomer
Preparation: MIR: capillary film
  FIR: 0.21 mm cell

165

Composition: diallyl phthalate
Use: monomer
Preparation: MIR: liquid film
  FIR: 0.21 mm cell

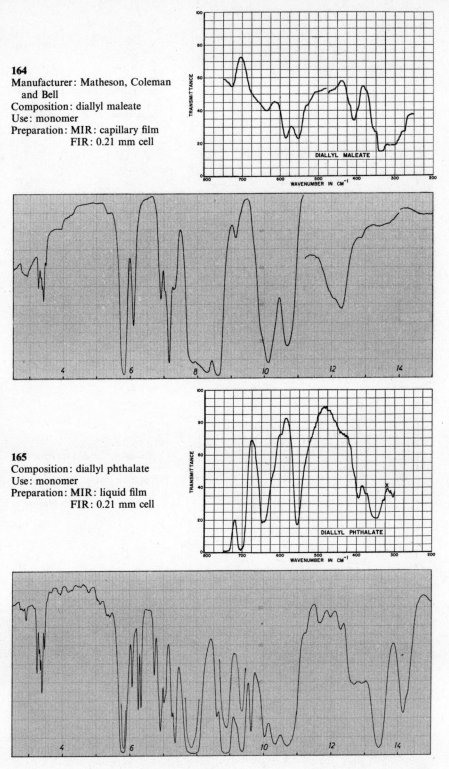

DIALLYL MALEATE

DIALLYL PHTHALATE

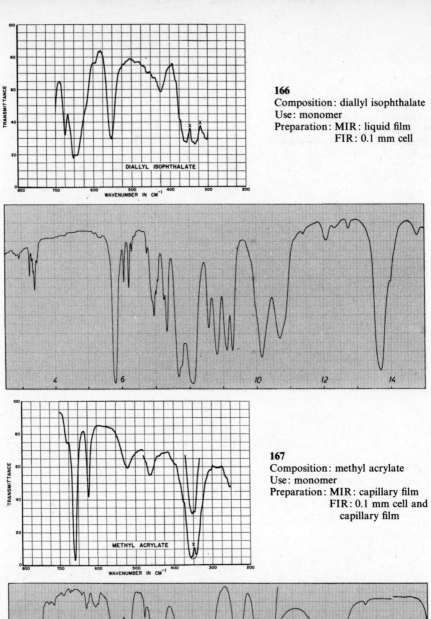

166

Composition: diallyl isophthalate
Use: monomer
Preparation: MIR: liquid film
           FIR: 0.1 mm cell

DIALLYL ISOPHTHALATE

167

Composition: methyl acrylate
Use: monomer
Preparation: MIR: capillary film
           FIR: 0.1 mm cell and
               capillary film

METHYL ACRYLATE

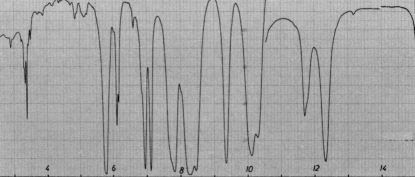

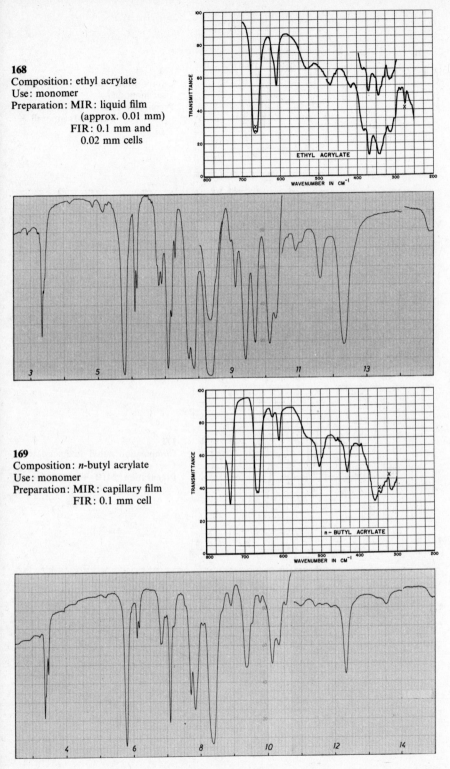

168
Composition: ethyl acrylate
Use: monomer
Preparation: MIR: liquid film
(approx. 0.01 mm)
FIR: 0.1 mm and
0.02 mm cells

ETHYL ACRYLATE

169
Composition: *n*-butyl acrylate
Use: monomer
Preparation: MIR: capillary film
FIR: 0.1 mm cell

n- BUTYL ACRYLATE

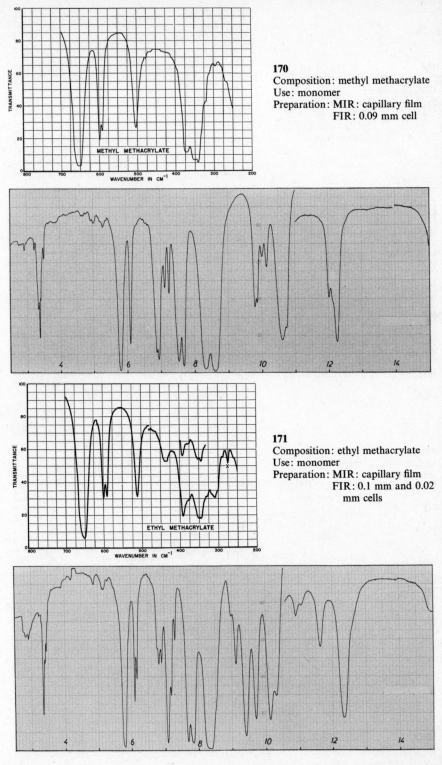

170
Composition: methyl methacrylate
Use: monomer
Preparation: MIR: capillary film
FIR: 0.09 mm cell

METHYL METHACRYLATE

171
Composition: ethyl methacrylate
Use: monomer
Preparation: MIR: capillary film
FIR: 0.1 mm and 0.02
mm cells

ETHYL METHACRYLATE

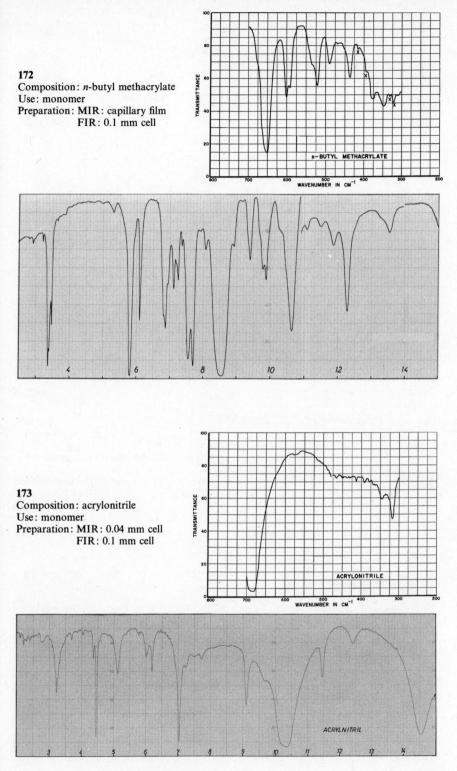

172
Composition: *n*-butyl methacrylate
Use: monomer
Preparation: MIR: capillary film
FIR: 0.1 mm cell

n-BUTYL METHACRYLATE

173
Composition: acrylonitrile
Use: monomer
Preparation: MIR: 0.04 mm cell
FIR: 0.1 mm cell

ACRYLONITRILE

ACRYLNITRIL

7

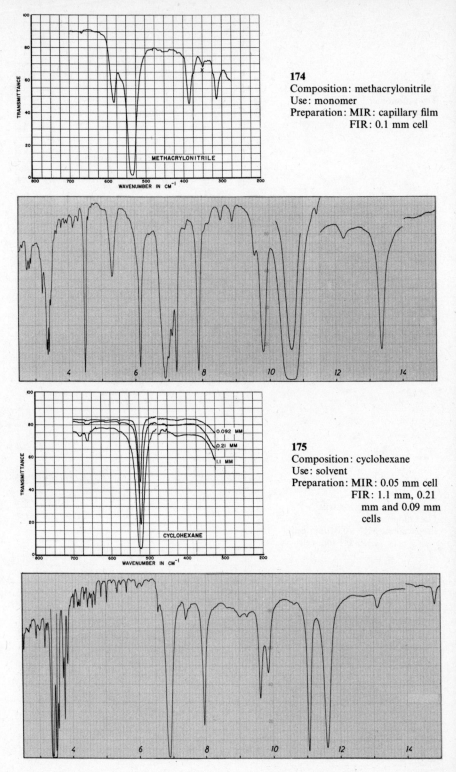

174
Composition: methacrylonitrile
Use: monomer
Preparation: MIR: capillary film
FIR: 0.1 mm cell

175
Composition: cyclohexane
Use: solvent
Preparation: MIR: 0.05 mm cell
FIR: 1.1 mm, 0.21
mm and 0.09 mm
cells

176

Composition: paraffin oil (Nujol)
Use: infrared preparations
Preparation: MIR: 0.05 mm cell
FIR: 1.1 mm and
0.21 mm cells

177

Composition: methylene chloride
Use: solvent
Preparation: MIR: 0.05 mm cell;
capillary film of
diluted solution in
cyclohexane (for
7.9 μ and 13.4 μ)
FIR: 1.1 mm, 0.21
mm, and 0.09 mm
cells

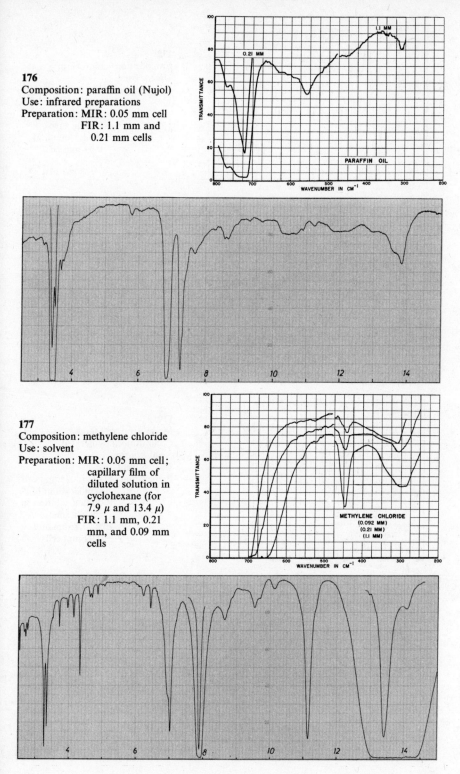

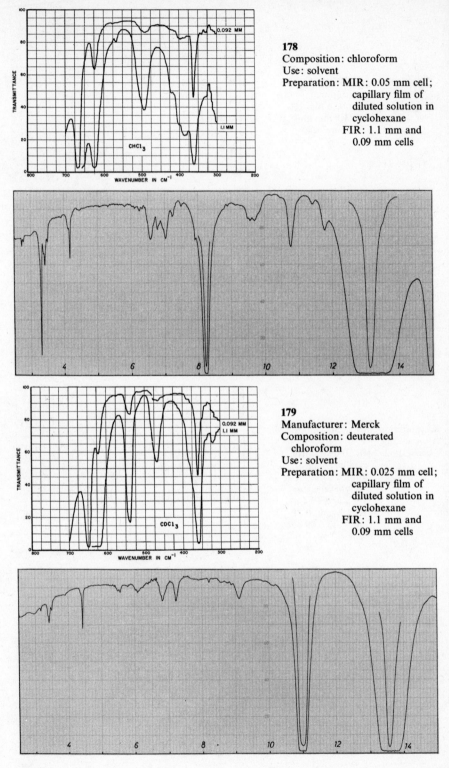

178
Composition: chloroform
Use: solvent
Preparation: MIR: 0.05 mm cell;
capillary film of
diluted solution in
cyclohexane
FIR: 1.1 mm and
0.09 mm cells

179
Manufacturer: Merck
Composition: deuterated
chloroform
Use: solvent
Preparation: MIR: 0.025 mm cell;
capillary film of
diluted solution in
cyclohexane
FIR: 1.1 mm and
0.09 mm cells

180

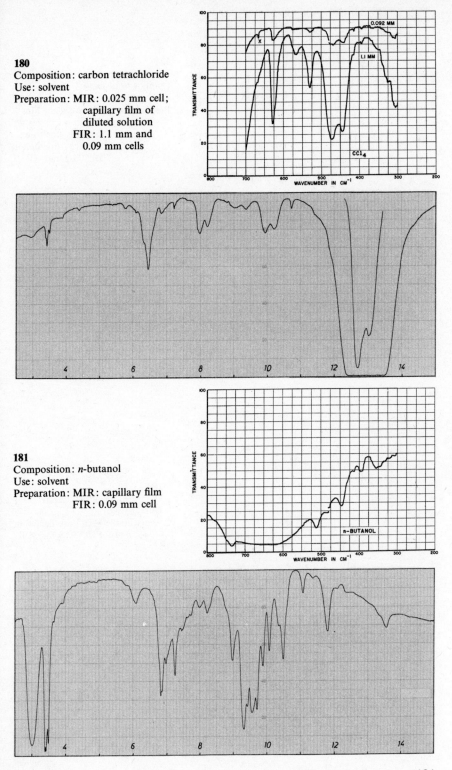

180

Composition: carbon tetrachloride
Use: solvent
Preparation: MIR: 0.025 mm cell;
capillary film of
diluted solution
FIR: 1.1 mm and
0.09 mm cells

181

Composition: *n*-butanol
Use: solvent
Preparation: MIR: capillary film
FIR: 0.09 mm cell

181

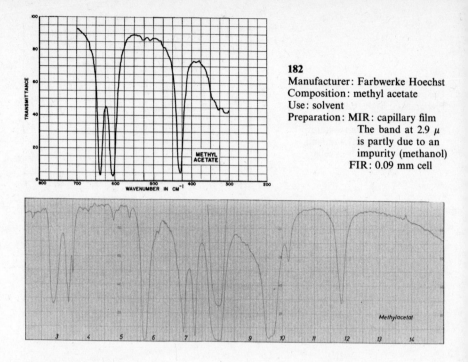

182
Manufacturer: Farbwerke Hoechst
Composition: methyl acetate
Use: solvent
Preparation: MIR: capillary film
The band at 2.9 μ
is partly due to an
impurity (methanol)
FIR: 0.09 mm cell

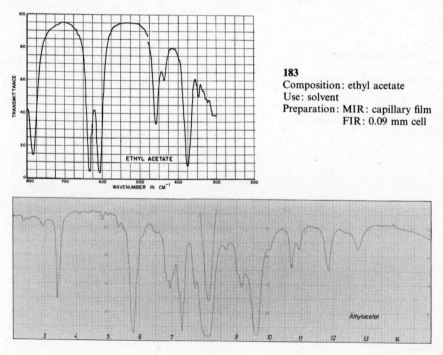

183
Composition: ethyl acetate
Use: solvent
Preparation: MIR: capillary film
FIR: 0.09 mm cell

184

Composition: *n*-butyl acetate
Use: solvent
Preparation: MIR: 0.025 mm cell;
capillary film of
diluted solution in
CS$_2$
FIR: 0.09 mm cell

185

Composition: 1,4-Dioxane
Use: solvent
Preparation: MIR: capillary film
FIR: 1.1 mm, 0.21
mm, and 0.09 mm
cells

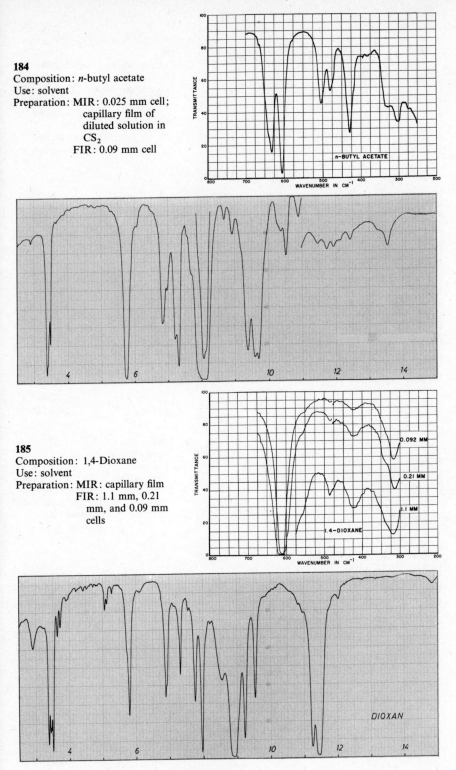

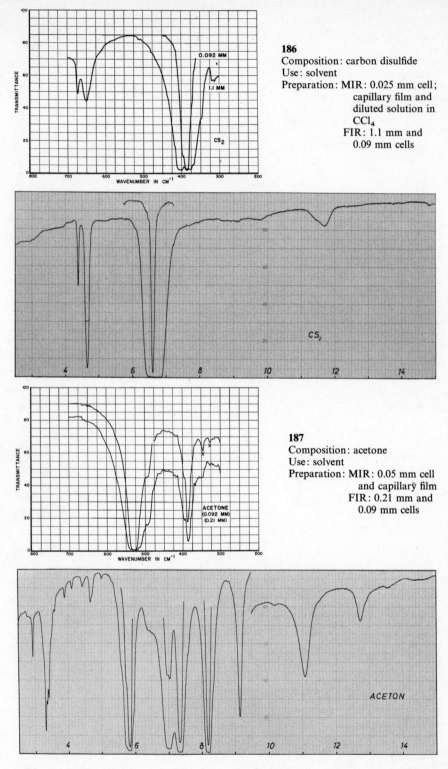

186
Composition: carbon disulfide
Use: solvent
Preparation: MIR: 0.025 mm cell;
    capillary film and
    diluted solution in
    CCl$_4$
    FIR: 1.1 mm and
    0.09 mm cells

187
Composition: acetone
Use: solvent
Preparation: MIR: 0.05 mm cell
    and capillary film
    FIR: 0.21 mm and
    0.09 mm cells

184

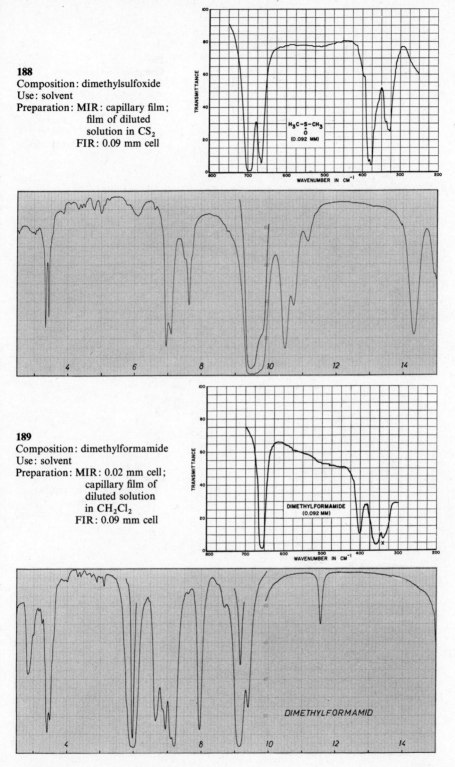

188
Composition: dimethylsulfoxide
Use: solvent
Preparation: MIR: capillary film;
film of diluted
solution in CS₂
FIR: 0.09 mm cell

H₃C–S–CH₃
‖
O
(0.092 MM)

189
Composition: dimethylformamide
Use: solvent
Preparation: MIR: 0.02 mm cell;
capillary film of
diluted solution
in CH₂Cl₂
FIR: 0.09 mm cell

DIMETHYLFORMAMIDE
(0.092 MM)

DIMETHYLFORMAMID

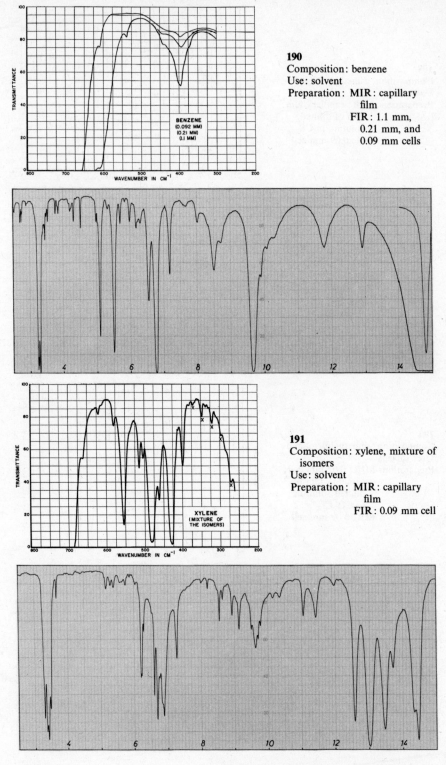

190
Composition: benzene
Use: solvent
Preparation: MIR: capillary
        film
       FIR: 1.1 mm,
          0.21 mm, and
          0.09 mm cells

BENZENE
(0.092 MM)
(0.21 MM)
(1.1 MM)

TRANSMITTANCE
WAVENUMBER IN CM⁻¹

191
Composition: xylene, mixture of
    isomers
Use: solvent
Preparation: MIR: capillary
        film
       FIR: 0.09 mm cell

XYLENE
(MIXTURE OF
THE ISOMERS)

TRANSMITTANCE
WAVENUMBER IN CM⁻¹

192
Composition: pyridine
Use: solvent
Preparation: MIR: capillary film
FIR: 0.09 mm cell

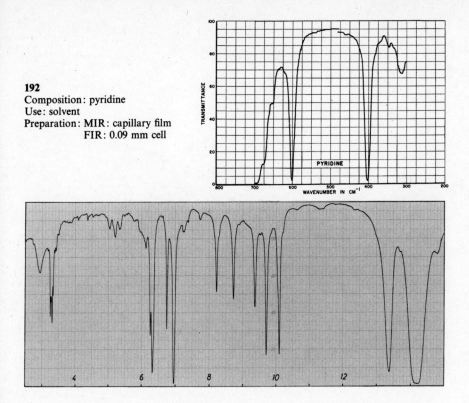

PYRIDINE

Appendix B

PICTORIAL SPECTRAL CHARTS OF
POLYMERS, RESINS, AND
RELATED MATERIALS

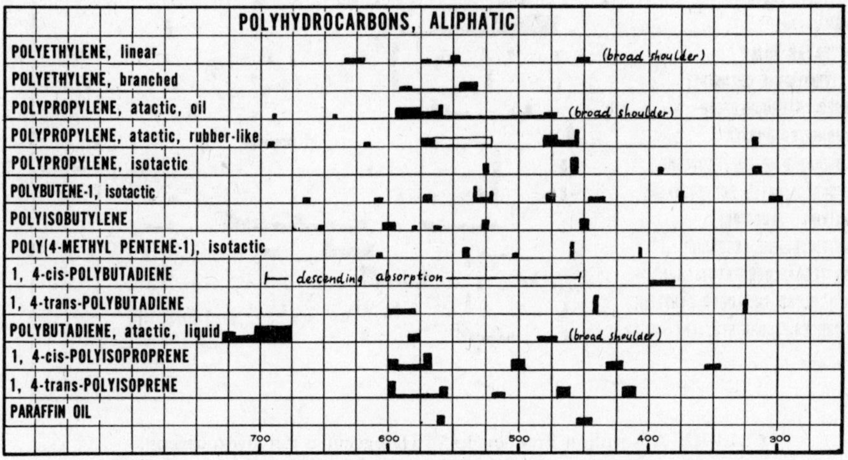

Chart I. Absorption Frequencies of Aliphatic Polyhydrocarbons

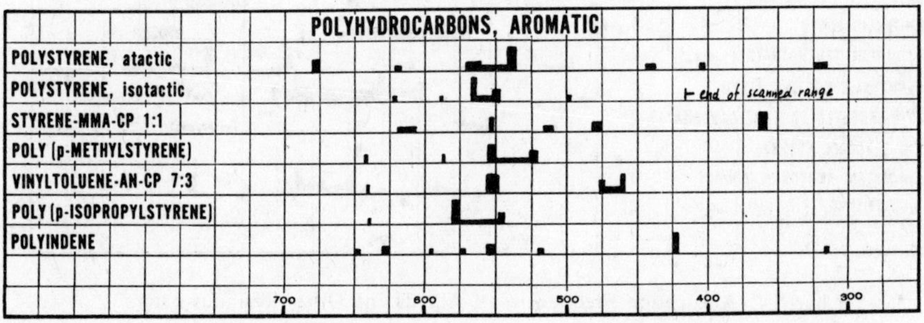

Chart II. Absorption Frequencies of Aromatic Polyhydrocarbons

191

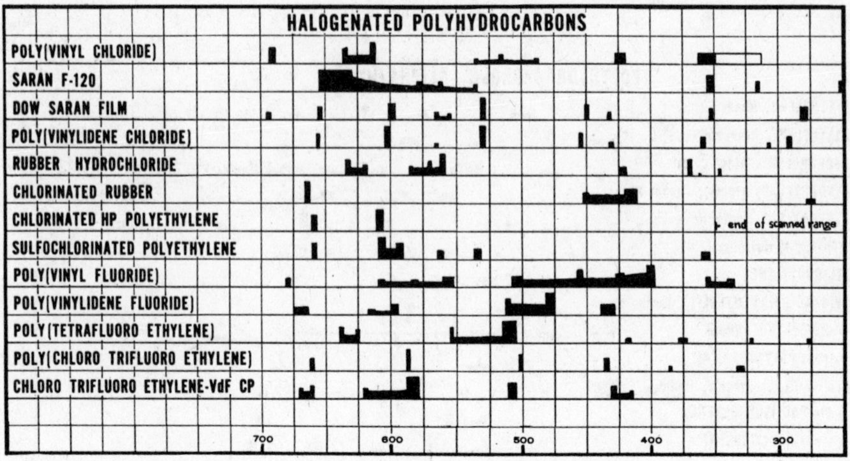

Chart III. Absorption Frequencies of Halogenated Polyhydrocarbons

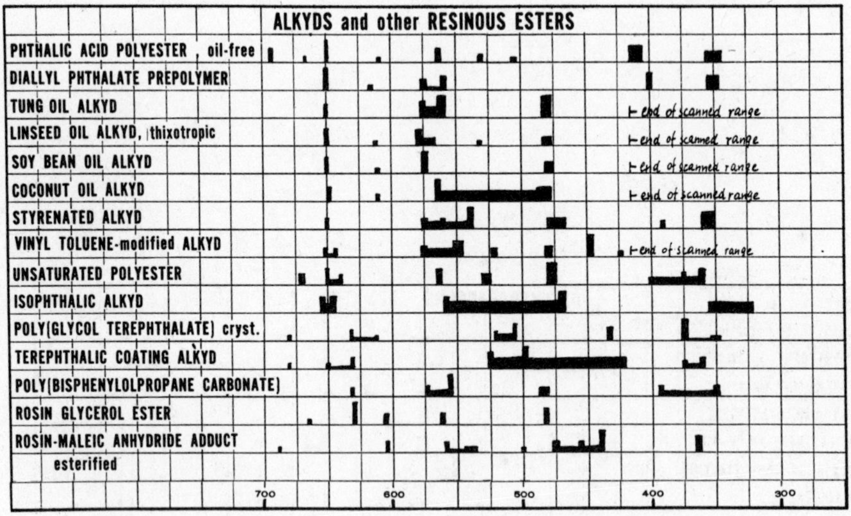

Chart IV. Absorption Frequencies of Alkyds and Other Resinous Esters

192

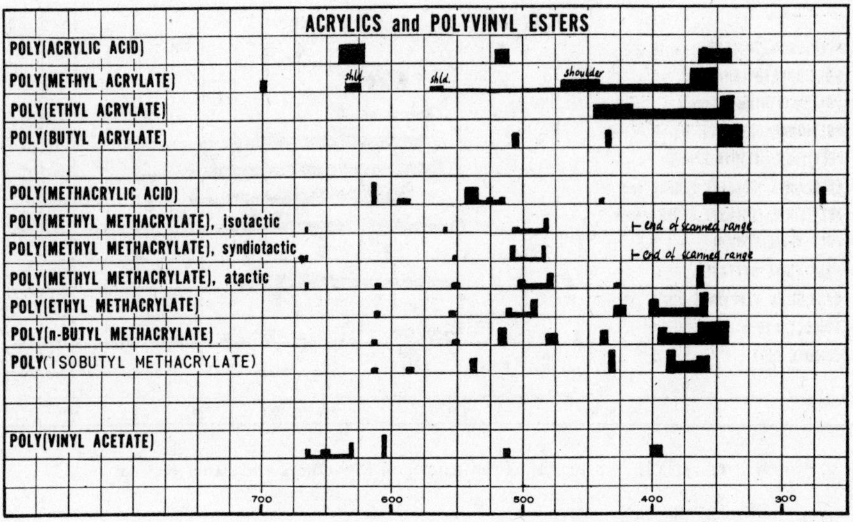

Chart V. Absorption Frequencies of Acrylics and Polyvinyl Esters

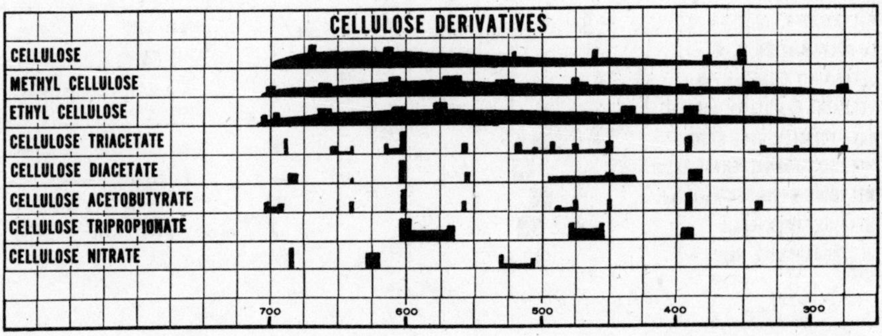

Chart VI. Absorption Frequencies of Cellulose Derivatives

193

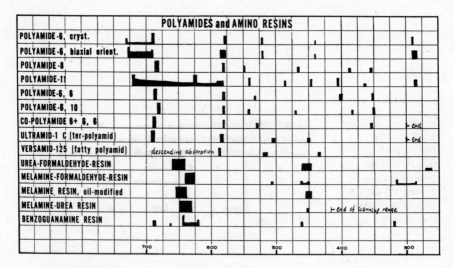

POLYETHERS and ETHER RESINS

	700	600	500	400	300
POLY(OXYMETHYLENE), Delrin					
POLY(OXYETHYLENE), liq.					
POLY(OXYETHYLENE), cryst.					
POLY(OXYPROPYLENE), liq.					
POLY(VINYL METHYL ETHER)					
POLY(VINYL ISOBUTYL ETHER), low					
POLY(VINYL ISOBUTYL ETHER), high					
POLY VINYL FORMAL					
POLY VINYL BUTYRAL					
EPOXIDIZED VEGETABLE OIL					
EPIKOTE 828					
EPIKOTE 1007					

Chart VII. Absorption Frequencies of Polyethers and Ether Resins

POLYAMIDES and AMINO RESINS

	700	600	500	400	300
POLYAMIDE-6, cryst.					
POLYAMIDE-6, biaxial orient.					
POLYAMIDE-8					
POLYAMIDE-11					
POLYAMIDE-6, 6					
POLYAMIDE-6, 10					
CO-POLYAMIDE 6+ 6, 6					⊢ end
ULTRAMID-1 C (ter-polyamid)					⊢ end
VERSAMID-125 (fatty polyamid)	descending absorption				
UREA-FORMALDEHYDE-RESIN					
MELAMINE-FORMALDEHYDE-RESIN					
MELAMINE RESIN, oil-modified					
MELAMINE-UREA RESIN				⊢ end of scanning range	
BENZOGUANAMINE RESIN					

Chart VIII. Absorption Frequencies of Polyamide and Amino Resins

194

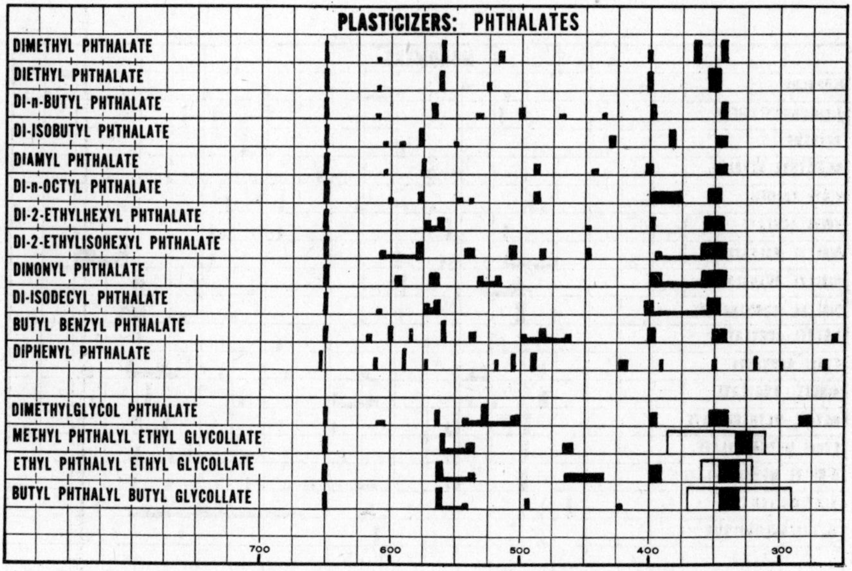

Chart IX. Absorption Frequencies of Plasticizers: Phthalates

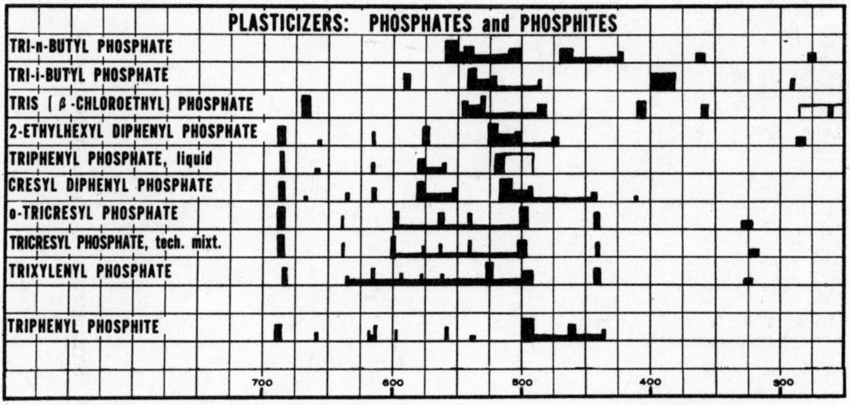

Chart X. Absorption Frequencies of Plasticizers: Phosphates and Phosphites

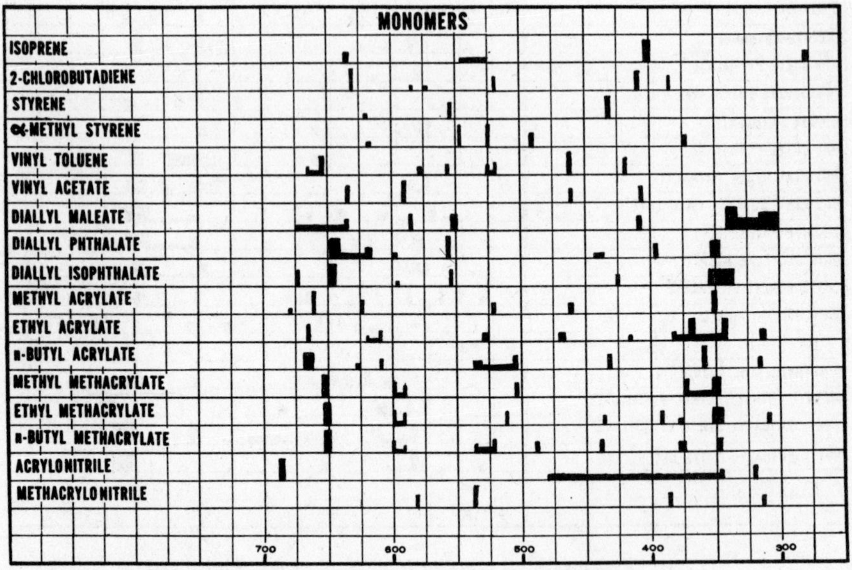

Chart XI. Absorption Frequencies of Monomers

Appendix C

WAVENUMBER/WAVELENGTH CONVERSION TABLE

Wavelength (μ)	Wavenumber (cm^{-1})									
	0	1	2	3	4	5	6	7	8	9
2.0	5000	4975	4950	4926	4902	4878	4854	4831	4808	4785
2.1	4762	4739	4717	4695	4673	4651	4630	4608	4587	4566
2.2	4545	4525	4505	4484	4464	4444	4425	4405	4386	4367
2.3	4348	4329	4310	4292	4274	4255	4237	4219	4202	4184
2.4	4167	4149	4132	4115	4098	4082	4065	4049	4032	4016
2.5	4000	3984	3968	3953	3937	3922	3906	3891	3876	3861
2.6	3846	3831	3817	3802	3788	3774	3759	3745	3731	3717
2.7	3704	3690	3676	3663	3650	3636	3623	3610	3597	3584
2.8	3571	3559	3546	3534	3521	3509	3497	3484	3472	3460
2.9	3448	3436	3425	3413	3401	3390	3378	3367	3356	3344
3.0	3333	3322	3311	3300	3289	3279	3268	3257	3247	3236
3.1	3226	3215	3205	3195	3185	3175	3165	3155	3145	3135
3.2	3125	3115	3106	3096	3086	3077	3067	3058	3049	3040
3.3	3030	3021	3012	3003	2994	2985	2976	2967	2959	2950
3.4	2941	2933	2924	2915	2907	2899	2890	2882	2874	2865
3.5	2857	2849	2841	2833	2825	2817	2809	2801	2793	2786
3.6	2778	2770	2762	2755	2747	2740	2732	2725	2717	2710
3.7	2703	2695	2688	2681	2674	2667	2660	2653	2646	2639
3.8	2632	2625	2618	2611	2604	2597	2591	2584	2577	2571
3.9	2564	2558	2551	2545	2538	2532	2525	2519	2513	2506
4.0	2500	2494	2488	2481	2475	2469	2463	2457	2451	2445
4.1	2439	2433	2427	2421	2415	2410	2404	2398	2392	2387
4.2	2381	2375	2370	2364	2358	2353	2347	2342	2336	2331
4.3	2326	2320	2315	2309	2304	2299	2294	2288	2283	2278
4.4	2273	2268	2262	2257	2252	2247	2242	2237	2232	2227
4.5	2222	2217	2212	2208	2203	2198	2193	2188	2183	2179
4.6	2174	2169	2165	2160	2155	2151	2146	2141	2137	2132
4.7	2128	2123	2119	2114	2110	2105	2101	2096	2092	2088
4.8	2083	2079	2075	2070	2066	2062	2058	2053	2049	2045
4.9	2041	2037	2033	2028	2024	2020	2016	2012	2008	2004
5.0	2000	1996	1992	1988	1984	1980	1976	1972	1969	1965
5.1	1961	1957	1953	1949	1946	1942	1938	1934	1931	1927
5.2	1923	1919	1916	1912	1908	1905	1901	1898	1894	1890
5.3	1887	1883	1880	1876	1873	1869	1866	1862	1859	1855
5.4	1852	1848	1845	1842	1838	1835	1832	1828	1825	1821
5.5	1818	1815	1812	1808	1805	1802	1799	1795	1792	1789
5.6	1786	1783	1779	1776	1773	1770	1767	1764	1761	1757
5.7	1754	1751	1748	1745	1742	1739	1736	1733	1730	1727
5.8	1724	1721	1718	1715	1712	1709	1706	1704	1701	1698
5.9	1695	1692	1689	1686	1684	1681	1678	1675	1672	1669
	0	1	2	3	4	5	6	7	8	9

From: Koji Nakanishi: Holden-Day, Inc., San Francisco and Nankodo Company Limited, Tokyo (by the courtesy of Drs. M. Kishita and Y. Kuroda, Nagoya University).

Wavelength (μ)	Wavenumber (cm^{-1})									
	0	1	2	3	4	5	6	7	8	9
6.0	1667	1664	1661	1658	1656	1653	1650	1647	1645	1642
6.1	1639	1637	1634	1631	1629	1626	1623	1621	1618	1616
6.2	1613	1610	1608	1605	1603	1600	1597	1595	1592	1590
6.3	1587	1585	1582	1580	1577	1575	1572	1570	1567	1565
6.4	1563	1560	1558	1555	1553	1550	1548	1546	1543	1541
6.5	1538	1536	1534	1531	1529	1527	1524	1522	1520	1517
6.6	1515	1513	1511	1508	1506	1504	1502	1499	1497	1495
6.7	1493	1490	1488	1486	1484	1481	1479	1477	1475	1473
6.8	1471	1468	1466	1464	1462	1460	1458	1456	1453	1451
6.9	1449	1447	1445	1443	1441	1439	1437	1435	1433	1431
7.0	1429	1427	1425	1422	1420	1418	1416	1414	1412	1410
7.1	1408	1406	1404	1403	1401	1399	1397	1395	1393	1391
7.2	1389	1387	1385	1383	1381	1379	1377	1376	1374	1372
7.3	1370	1368	1366	1364	1362	1361	1359	1357	1355	1353
7.4	1351	1350	1348	1346	1344	1342	1340	1339	1337	1335
7.5	1333	1332	1330	1328	1326	1325	1323	1321	1319	1318
7.6	1316	1314	1312	1311	1309	1307	1305	1304	1302	1300
7.7	1299	1297	1295	1294	1292	1290	1289	1287	1285	1284
7.8	1282	1280	1279	1277	1276	1274	1272	1271	1269	1267
7.9	1266	1264	1263	1261	1259	1258	1256	1255	1253	1252
8.0	1250	1248	1247	1245	1244	1242	1241	1239	1238	1236
8.1	1235	1233	1232	1230	1229	1227	1225	1224	1222	1221
8.2	1220	1218	1217	1215	1214	1212	1211	1209	1208	1206
8.3	1205	1203	1202	1200	1199	1198	1196	1195	1193	1192
8.4	1190	1189	1188	1186	1185	1183	1182	1181	1179	1178
8.5	1176	1175	1174	1172	1171	1170	1168	1167	1166	1164
8.6	1163	1161	1160	1159	1157	1156	1155	1153	1152	1151
8.7	1149	1148	1147	1145	1144	1143	1142	1140	1139	1138
8.8	1136	1135	1134	1133	1131	1130	1129	1127	1126	1125
8.9	1124	1122	1121	1120	1119	1117	1116	1115	1114	1112
9.0	1111	1110	1109	1107	1106	1105	1104	1103	1101	1100
9.1	1099	1098	1096	1095	1094	1093	1092	1091	1089	1088
9.2	1087	1086	1085	1083	1082	1081	1080	1079	1078	1076
9.3	1075	1074	1073	1072	1071	1070	1068	1067	1066	1065
9.4	1064	1063	1062	1060	1059	1058	1057	1056	1055	1054
9.5	1053	1052	1050	1049	1048	1047	1046	1045	1044	1043
9.6	1042	1041	1040	1038	1037	1036	1035	1034	1033	1032
9.7	1031	1030	1029	1028	1027	1026	1025	1024	1022	1021
9.8	1020	1019	1018	1017	1016	1015	1014	1013	1012	1011
9.9	1010	1009	1008	1007	1006	1005	1004	1003	1002	1001
	0	1	2	3	4	5	6	7	8	9

Wavelength (μ)	Wavenumber (cm^{-1})									
	0	1	2	3	4	5	6	7	8	9
10.0	1000.0	999.0	998.0	997.0	996.0	995.0	994.0	993.0	992.1	991.1
10.1	990.1	989.1	988.1	987.2	986.2	985.2	984.3	983.3	982.3	981.4
10.2	980.4	979.4	978.5	977.5	976.6	975.6	974.7	973.7	972.8	971.8
10.3	970.9	969.0	969.0	968.1	967.1	966.2	965.3	964.3	963.4	962.5
10.4	961.5	960.6	959.7	958.8	957.9	956.9	956.0	955.1	954.2	953.3
10.5	952.4	951.5	950.6	949.7	948.8	947.9	947.0	946.1	945.2	944.3
10.6	943.4	942.5	941.6	940.7	939.8	939.0	938.1	937.2	936.3	935.5
10.7	934.6	933.7	932.8	932.0	931.1	930.2	929.4	928.5	927.6	926.8
10.8	925.9	925.1	924.2	923.4	922.5	921.7	920.8	920.0	919.1	918.3
10.9	917.4	916.6	915.8	914.9	914.1	913.2	912.4	911.6	910.7	909.9
11.0	909.1	908.3	907.4	906.6	905.8	905.0	904.2	903.3	902.5	901.7
11.1	900.9	900.1	899.3	898.5	897.7	896.9	896.1	895.3	894.5	893.7
11.2	892.9	892.1	891.3	890.5	889.7	888.9	888.1	887.3	886.5	885.7
11.3	885.0	884.2	883.4	882.6	881.8	881.1	880.3	879.5	878.7	878.0
11.4	877.2	876.4	875.7	874.9	874.1	873.4	872.6	871.8	871.1	870.3
11.5	869.6	868.8	868.1	867.3	866.6	865.8	865.1	864.3	863.6	862.8
11.6	862.1	861.3	860.6	859.8	859.1	858.4	857.6	856.9	856.2	855.4
11.7	854.7	854.0	853.2	852.5	851.8	851.1	850.3	849.6	848.9	848.2
11.8	847.5	846.7	846.0	845.3	844.6	843.9	843.2	842.5	841.8	841.0
11.9	840.3	839.6	838.9	838.2	837.5	836.8	836.1	835.4	834.7	834.0
12.0	833.3	832.6	831.9	831.3	830.6	829.9	829.2	828.5	827.8	827.1
12.1	826.4	825.8	825.1	824.4	823.7	823.0	822.4	821.7	821.0	820.3
12.2	819.7	819.0	818.3	817.7	817.0	816.3	815.7	815.0	814.3	813.7
12.3	813.0	812.3	811.7	811.0	810.4	809.7	809.1	808.4	807.8	807.1
12.4	806.5	805.8	805.2	804.5	803.9	803.2	802.6	801.9	801.3	800.6
12.5	800.0	799.4	798.7	798.1	797.4	796.8	796.2	795.5	794.9	794.3
12.6	793.7	793.0	792.4	791.8	791.1	790.5	789.9	789.3	788.6	788.0
12.7	787.4	786.8	786.2	785.5	784.9	784.3	783.7	783.1	782.5	781.9
12.8	781.3	780.6	780.0	779.4	778.8	778.2	777.6	777.0	776.4	775.8
12.9	775.2	774.6	774.0	773.4	772.8	772.2	771.6	771.0	770.4	769.8
13.0	769.2	768.6	768.0	767.5	766.9	766.3	765.7	765.1	764.5	763.9
13.1	763.4	762.8	762.2	761.6	761.0	760.5	759.9	759.3	758.7	758.2
13.2	757.6	757.0	756.4	755.9	755.3	754.7	754.1	753.6	753.0	752.4
13.3	751.9	751.3	750.8	750.2	749.6	749.1	748.5	747.9	747.4	746.8
13.4	746.3	745.7	745.2	744.6	744.0	743.5	742.9	742.4	741.8	741.3
13.5	740.7	740.2	739.6	739.1	738.6	738.0	737.5	736.9	736.4	735.8
13.6	735.3	734.8	734.2	733.7	733.1	732.6	732.1	731.5	731.0	730.5
13.7	729.9	729.4	728.9	728.3	727.8	727.3	726.7	726.2	725.7	725.2
13.8	724.6	724.1	723.6	723.1	722.5	722.0	721.5	721.0	720.5	719.9
13.9	719.4	718.9	718.4	717.9	717.4	716.8	716.3	715.8	715.3	714.8
14.0	714.3	713.8	713.3	712.8	712.3	711.7	711.2	710.7	710.2	709.7
14.1	709.2	708.7	708.2	707.7	707.2	706.7	706.2	705.7	705.2	704.7
14.2	704.2	703.7	703.2	702.7	702.2	701.8	701.3	700.8	700.3	699.8
14.3	699.3	698.8	698.3	697.8	697.4	696.9	696.4	695.9	695.4	694.9
14.4	694.4	694.0	693.5	693.0	692.5	692.0	691.6	691.1	690.6	690.1
14.5	689.7	689.2	688.7	688.2	687.8	687.3	686.8	686.3	685.9	685.4
14.6	684.9	684.5	684.0	683.5	683.1	682.6	682.1	681.7	681.2	680.7
14.7	680.3	679.8	679.3	678.9	678.4	678.0	677.5	677.0	676.6	676.1
14.8	675.7	675.2	674.8	674.3	673.9	673.4	672.9	672.5	672.0	671.6
14.9	671.1	670.7	670.2	669.8	669.3	668.9	668.4	668.0	667.6	667.1
	0	1	2	3	4	5	6	7	8	9

Wavelength (μ)	Wavenumber (cm^{-1})									
	0	1	2	3	4	5	6	7	8	9
15.0	666.7	666.2	665.8	665.3	664.9	664.5	664.0	663.6	663.1	662.7
15.1	662.3	661.8	661.4	660.9	660.5	660.1	659.6	659.2	658.8	658.3
15.2	657.9	657.5	657.0	656.6	656.2	655.7	655.3	654.9	654.5	654.0
15.3	653.6	653.2	652.7	652.3	651.9	651.5	651.0	650.6	650.2	649.8
15.4	649.4	648.9	648.5	648.1	647.7	647.2	646.8	646.4	646.0	645.6
15.5	645.2	644.7	644.3	643.9	643.5	643.1	642.7	642.3	641.8	641.4
15.6	641.0	640.6	640.2	639.8	639.4	639.0	638.6	638.2	637.8	637.3
15.7	636.9	636.5	636.1	635.7	635.3	634.9	634.5	634.1	633.7	633.3
15.8	632.9	632.5	632.1	631.7	631.3	630.9	630.5	630.1	629.7	629.3
15.9	628.9	628.5	628.1	627.7	627.4	627.0	626.6	626.2	625.8	625.4
16.0	625.0	624.6	624.2	623.8	623.4	623.1	622.7	622.3	621.9	621.5
16.1	621.1	620.7	620.3	620.0	619.6	619.2	618.8	618.4	618.0	617.7
16.2	617.3	616.9	616.5	616.1	615.8	615.4	615.0	614.6	614.3	613.9
16.3	613.5	613.1	612.7	612.4	612.0	611.6	611.2	610.9	610.5	610.1
16.4	609.8	609.4	609.0	608.6	608.3	607.9	607.5	607.2	606.8	606.4
16.5	606.1	605.7	605.3	605.0	604.6	604.2	603.9	603.5	603.1	602.8
16.6	602.4	602.0	601.7	601.3	601.0	600.6	600.2	599.9	599.5	599.2
16.7	598.8	598.4	598.1	597.7	597.4	597.0	596.7	596.3	595.9	595.6
16.8	595.2	594.9	594.5	594.2	593.8	593.5	593.1	592.8	592.4	592.1
16.9	591.7	591.4	591.0	590.7	590.3	590.0	589.6	589.3	588.9	588.6
17.0	588.2	587.9	587.5	587.2	586.9	586.5	586.2	585.8	585.5	585.1
17.1	584.8	584.5	584.1	583.8	583.4	583.1	582.8	582.4	582.1	581.7
17.2	581.4	581.1	580.7	580.4	580.0	579.7	579.4	579.0	578.7	578.4
17.3	578.0	577.7	577.4	577.0	576.7	576.4	576.0	575.7	575.4	575.0
17.4	574.7	574.4	574.1	573.7	573.4	573.1	572.7	572.4	572.1	571.8
17.5	571.4	571.1	570.8	570.5	570.1	569.8	569.5	569.2	568.8	568.5
17.6	568.2	567.9	567.5	567.2	566.9	566.6	566.3	565.9	565.6	565.3
17.7	565.0	564.7	564.3	564.0	563.7	563.4	563.1	562.7	562.4	562.1
17.8	561.8	561.5	561.2	560.9	560.5	560.2	559.9	559.6	559.3	559.0
17.9	558.7	558.3	558.0	557.7	557.4	557.1	556.8	556.5	556.2	555.9
18.0	555.6	555.2	554.9	554.6	554.3	554.0	553.7	553.4	553.1	552.8
18.1	552.5	552.2	551.9	551.6	551.3	551.0	550.7	550.4	550.1	549.8
18.2	549.5	549.1	548.8	548.5	548.2	547.9	547.6	547.3	547.0	546.7
18.3	546.4	546.1	545.9	545.6	545.3	545.0	544.7	544.4	544.1	543.8
18.4	543.5	543.2	542.9	542.6	542.3	542.0	541.7	541.4	541.1	540.8
18.5	540.5	540.2	540.0	539.7	539.4	539.1	538.8	538.5	538.2	537.9
18.6	537.6	537.3	537.1	536.8	536.5	536.2	535.9	535.6	535.3	535.0
18.7	534.8	534.5	534.2	533.9	533.6	533.3	533.0	532.8	532.5	532.2
18.8	531.9	531.6	531.3	531.1	530.8	530.5	530.2	529.9	529.7	529.4
18.9	529.1	528.8	528.5	528.3	528.0	527.7	527.4	527.1	526.9	526.6
19.0	526.3	526.0	525.8	525.5	525.2	524.9	524.7	524.4	524.1	523.8
19.1	523.6	523.3	523.0	522.7	522.5	522.2	521.9	521.6	521.4	521.1
19.2	520.8	520.6	520.3	520.0	519.8	519.5	519.2	518.9	518.7	518.4
19.3	518.1	517.9	517.6	517.3	517.1	516.8	516.5	516.3	516.0	515.7
19.4	515.5	515.2	514.9	514.7	514.4	514.1	513.9	513.6	513.3	513.1
19.5	512.8	512.6	512.3	512.0	511.8	511.5	511.2	511.0	510.7	510.5
19.6	510.2	509.9	509.7	509.4	509.2	508.9	508.6	508.4	508.1	507.9
19.7	507.6	507.4	507.1	506.8	506.6	506.3	506.1	505.8	505.6	505.3
19.8	505.1	504.8	504.5	504.3	504.0	503.8	503.5	503.3	503.0	502.8
19.9	502.5	502.3	502.0	501.8	501.5	501.3	501.0	500.8	500.5	500.3
	0	1	2	3	4	5	6	7	8	9

Wavelength (μ)	Wavenumber (cm⁻¹)									
	0	1	2	3	4	5	6	7	8	9
20.0	500.0	499.8	499.5	499.3	499.0	498.8	498.5	498.3	498.0	497.8
20.1	497.5	497.3	497.0	496.8	496.5	496.3	496.0	495.8	495.5	495.3
20.2	495.0	494.8	494.6	494.3	494.1	493.8	493.6	493.3	493.1	492.9
20.3	492.6	492.4	492.1	491.9	491.6	491.4	491.2	490.9	490.7	490.4
20.4	490.2	490.0	489.7	489.5	489.2	489.0	488.8	488.5	488.3	488.0
20.5	487.8	487.6	487.3	487.1	486.9	486.6	486.4	486.1	485.9	485.7
20.6	485.4	485.2	485.0	484.7	484.5	484.3	484.0	483.8	483.6	483.3
20.7	483.1	482.9	482.6	482.4	482.2	481.9	481.7	481.5	481.2	481.0
20.8	480.8	480.5	480.3	480.1	479.8	479.6	479.4	479.2	478.9	478.7
20.9	478.5	478.2	478.0	477.8	477.6	477.3	477.1	476.9	476.6	476.4
21.0	476.2	476.0	475.7	475.5	475.3	475.1	474.8	474.6	474.4	474.2
21.1	473.9	473.7	473.5	473.3	473.0	472.8	472.6	472.4	472.1	471.9
21.2	471.7	471.5	471.3	471.0	470.8	470.6	470.4	470.1	469.9	469.7
21.3	469.5	469.3	469.0	468.8	468.6	468.4	468.2	467.9	467.7	467.5
21.4	467.3	467.1	466.9	466.6	466.4	466.2	466.0	465.8	465.5	465.3
21.5	465.1	464.9	464.7	464.5	464.3	464.0	463.8	463.6	463.4	463.2
21.6	463.0	462.7	462.5	462.3	462.1	461.9	461.7	461.5	461.3	461.0
21.7	460.8	460.6	460.4	460.2	460.0	459.8	459.6	459.3	459.1	458.9
21.8	458.7	458.5	458.3	458.1	457.9	457.7	457.5	457.2	457.0	456.8
21.9	456.6	456.4	456.2	456.0	455.8	455.6	455.4	455.2	455.0	454.8
22.0	454.5	454.3	454.1	453.9	453.7	453.5	453.3	453.1	452.9	452.7
22.1	452.5	452.3	452.1	451.9	451.7	451.5	451.3	451.1	450.9	450.7
22.2	450.5	450.2	450.0	449.8	449.6	449.4	449.2	449.0	448.8	448.6
22.3	448.4	448.2	448.0	447.8	447.6	447.4	447.2	447.0	446.8	446.6
22.4	446.4	446.2	446.0	445.8	445.6	445.4	445.2	445.0	444.8	444.6
22.5	444.4	444.2	444.0	443.9	443.7	443.5	443.3	443.1	442.9	442.7
22.6	442.5	442.3	442.1	441.9	441.7	441.5	441.3	441.1	440.9	440.7
22.7	440.5	440.3	440.1	439.9	439.8	439.6	439.4	439.2	439.0	438.8
22.8	438.6	438.4	438.2	438.0	437.8	437.6	437.4	437.3	437.1	436.9
22.9	436.7	436.5	436.3	436.1	435.9	435.7	435.5	435.4	435.2	435.0
23.0	434.8	434.6	434.4	434.2	434.0	433.8	433.7	433.5	433.3	433.1
23.1	432.9	432.7	432.5	432.3	432.2	432.0	431.8	431.6	431.4	431.2
23.2	431.0	430.8	430.7	430.5	430.3	430.1	429.9	429.7	429.6	429.4
23.3	429.2	429.0	428.8	428.6	428.4	428.3	428.1	427.9	427.7	427.5
23.4	427.4	427.2	427.0	426.8	426.6	426.4	426.3	426.1	425.9	425.7
23.5	425.5	425.4	425.2	425.0	424.8	424.6	424.4	424.3	424.1	423.9
23.6	423.7	423.5	423.4	423.2	423.0	422.8	422.7	422.5	422.3	422.1
23.7	421.9	421.8	421.6	421.4	421.2	421.1	420.9	420.7	420.5	420.3
23.8	420.2	420.0	419.8	419.6	419.5	419.3	419.1	418.9	418.8	418.6
23.9	418.4	418.2	418.1	417.9	417.7	417.5	417.4	417.2	417.0	416.8
24.0	416.7	416.5	416.3	416.1	416.0	415.8	415.6	415.5	415.3	415.1
24.1	414.9	414.8	414.6	414.4	414.3	414.1	413.9	413.7	413.6	413.4
24.2	413.2	413.1	412.9	412.7	412.5	412.4	412.2	412.0	411.9	411.7
24.3	411.5	411.4	411.2	411.0	410.8	410.7	410.5	410.3	410.2	410.0
24.4	409.8	409.7	409.5	409.3	409.2	409.0	408.8	408.7	408.5	408.3
24.5	408.2	408.0	407.8	407.7	407.5	407.3	407.2	407.0	406.8	406.7
24.6	406.5	406.3	406.2	406.0	405.8	405.7	405.5	405.4	405.2	405.0
24.7	404.9	404.7	404.5	404.4	404.2	404.0	403.9	403.7	403.6	403.4
24.8	403.2	403.1	402.9	402.7	402.6	402.4	402.3	402.1	401.9	401.8
24.9	401.6	401.4	401.3	401.1	401.0	400.8	400.6	400.5	400.3	400.2
	0	1	2	3	4	5	6	7	8	9

Index

Bold figures refer to spectra numbers in Appendix A

Date Due